# HUMAN HEREDITY

C. O. CARTER

WITH FOUR PLATES AND
SEVENTY-TWO TEXT FIGURES

PENGUIN BOOKS

Penguin Books Ltd, Harmondsworth, Middlesex, England
Penguin Books Inc., 7110 Ambassador Road, Baltimore, Maryland 21207, U.S.A.
Penguin Books Australia Ltd, Ringwood, Victoria, Australia

—

First published 1962
Reprinted 1963, 1965, 1967, 1969

—

Copyright © C. O. Carter, 1962

—

Made and printed in Great Britain
by Cox & Wyman Ltd,
London, Reading and Fakenham
Set in Monotype Times

PELICAN BOOKS

# HUMAN HEREDITY

Cedric Carter is a member of the staff of the
Medical Research Council and works at a London
children's hospital. He was born in Port Said in
1917 and educated at the Institution Sainte Marie
near Toulon, at Winchester and Queen's College,
Oxford, and at St Thomas's Hospital, London.
His interest in heredity and eugenics began at
school. After wartime service, mostly as a Medical
Officer with the 8th Indian Division, he took a
higher degree in medicine and then turned to
research into the genetics of children's diseases.
He is also interested in the genetics of normal
qualities of social importance, and has been general
secretary of the Eugenics Society. He is married
and has seven children.

# Contents

## *Editorial Foreword*

WE all tend to take the commonplace and familiar in human experience for granted and cease to wonder at it. But, when one stops to think about these things, and asks for an explanation of them, again and again one finds that it is the most common and familiar which prove most difficult to account for in scientific terms. Heredity is an outstanding example of this fact. All species breed more or less true to type. Indeed, reproduction down the generations is one of the great characteristics of living things. On the other hand, individual variation does occur, and it is on variation of a certain kind that natural selection has worked to lead to organic evolution. In this book, which is bound to appeal to a very large circle of readers, Dr Carter explains in simple terms what is known about this extraordinary phenomenon, with particular reference to man.

In the first place his book must make an appeal to every thinking layman. For we have all inherited, not only our ordinary human characteristics, both physical and mental, from our parents, but also some of those characteristics which are peculiarly our own as the result of the complex gene pattern whence we are individually derived. Most of us, too, have had or will have children, and have passed or will pass on to them some of the characteristics which now seem peculiarly ours. Dr Carter's book explains all this, in so far as it is capable of explanation as yet, and helps us to distinguish, where the causation of human variation is concerned, between genetic factors and the influence of environment on individual development.

In the second place this book will appeal to sociologists.

To what extent can the human race be modified by control of environment? Or, can it be improved only by the control of human mating? Some seem to think environment all-important in this matter; others take their stand on eugenics, and tend to ignore the importance of environmental influence. Dr Carter's book will help the reader to take a balanced view in a field where a rational outlook is very much required. In the third place, it will appeal to all students of biological science. For, biologically speaking, man is a good example of an animal, and in it he will find a simple up-to-date account of the phenomenon of heredity in general.

Last but not least, to the medical student and practising doctor it will come as a ray of light in the darkness. Hitherto they have been regaled and oppressed by books on genetics dealing with the inheritance of odd conditions and rare characteristics, most of them extremely difficult to understand. But this book deals in a simple way with the familiar: with the inheritance of intelligence, constitution, and some of the common diseases which the doctor meets. Further, disease can be defined only as an alteration in an individual for the worse, as judged on human standards, and that must be due to some fault in the genetic plan whence the individual is derived, or to some adverse factor in the environment into which he has been born, or to interaction between these two rival factors. It is true that some common diseases *are* due to simple genetic factors; true also that some others *are* due to simple adverse factors in a man's environment. But the pendulum of medical opinion is fast swinging away from the idea of single simple causes. Most diseases are bred of complex interaction between genetic predisposition and adverse factors in environment. A proper understanding of human heredity is becoming increasingly important to a proper understanding of human disease.

A. E. CLARK-KENNEDY

# Acknowledgements

GRATEFUL acknowledgement is made to Dr H. Lehmann of St Bartholomew's Hospital for Plates 1 and 4a; to Dr Lehmann and the McGraw-Hill Publishing Co. Ltd for permission to reproduce Plate 4b from *The Metabolic Basis of Inherited Disease*, Stanbury, Wyngaarden, and Fredrickson (1960, McGraw-Hill Book Company, Inc.); to Mr J. L. Hamerton of Guy's Hospital for Plate 2; to the Department of Medical Illustration, the Hospital for Sick Children, and the family concerned, for Plate 3.

I am indebted to the Editor of the Penguin medical series, Dr A. E. Clark-Kennedy, for his kindly encouragement. Grateful thanks are due to Mrs K. A. Evans for her untiring help with the preparation of the manuscript and to those who kindly read and criticized it, particularly Dr H. Blyth, Dr K. Hutton, and my wife.

All those who work in the field of medical genetics owe much to the ideas of the two British pioneers, Dr J. A. Fraser Roberts and Professor L. S. Penrose, who, however, bear no responsibility for any controversial opinions expressed in this book. My concepts of eugenics have greatly benefited from discussions with Dr C. P. Blacker.

# CHAPTER 1

## Inheritance: How We can Learn from Twins

IN general, children resemble their parents. This is often more evident to others than to the parents themselves. A family doctor, and even more a children's specialist, who sees a succession of mothers and children during his consulting hours and visits, is constantly struck by these resemblances of features, body-build, and mannerisms. People change as they age, and these resemblances would be even more striking if one could see, say, a mother at the age of six and her daughter at the same age. Parents who are lucky enough to have photographs of themselves as children will be able to make these comparisons. There are also many exceptions to this general resemblance. A particular child may resemble neither parent, at any rate for some of his characteristics. The scientific study of heredity, which is called genetics, attempts to analyse and explain these likenesses and, equally important, the unlikenesses.

There is, of course, more than one cause of likeness between parent and child. The first main cause is true genetic inheritance, a potentiality for growth along certain lines transmitted from parent to child in the germ cells. The second main cause is cultural inheritance, the tendency of children to learn from and imitate their parents and also to have social experiences, such as standard of living and type of schooling, of much the same kind as their parents. As knowledge of human heredity grows, it is becoming increasingly possible to distinguish likenesses due to heredity from likenesses due to similar external influences, physical, social, and cultural. The latter groups of influences are collectively called environmental.

11

It has become clear from animal as well as human studies that both inherited and environmental factors influence a child's development for almost all characteristics. It is not possible to give any general answer to the question as to which is more important, heredity or environment. Severe inherited defect or severe environmental damage may each prevent normal development. It is possible, however, and useful, to divide individual qualities into three groups:

(1) those in which human beings resemble or differ from each other because of differences in inherited factors; such a quality is the colour of the eyes, and no environmental factors are known to influence eye-colour appreciably.
(2) those in which people resemble each other or differ from each other almost entirely because of differences in environment; such a quality is language.
(3) those in which people resemble each other or differ from each other because of differences of both heredity and environment; such qualities are stature and intelligence-test score during school age.

The qualities which may be allotted to the first two groups are rather few compared with those that go into the third, mixed group. In the large third group, the relative importance of inherited and environmental difference as a cause of variation will change with the group of children or adults being studied. For example, in a group of healthy children who have been well fed all their lives, variation in height will, in most part, be due to differences in inheritance. In a group where some have been well fed but others have been chronically undernourished, the difference in height between members of the group may well be due more to these variations in nurture than to genetic differences. In the same way, where a group of children have had a uniform type of schooling and very similar home backgrounds, it is likely that differences in inheritance will be responsible for much of the variation in intelligence-test score; this is particularly the case for children in the same family. But any investigator must always be on the look-out for un-expected differences in environment, even, for example, in a group of children reared together in an orphanage.

*Early twin studies*

In animal experiments it is possible to make an analysis more precise by largely eliminating variations in environment, and so to observe differences due to variations in heredity alone. It is also possible to study the effects of varied environments, for example different diets, on strains of animals which have been intensively inbred so that complication from genetic variation is much reduced. With human beings a group with a really uniform environment is perhaps never found but, fortunately, there are a number of individuals with the same inheritance. These are 'identical' twins, derived from a single embryo which has divided in half early in development and each half of which has gone on to form a separate child. The strong general resemblance of 'identical' twins in features, body-build, and the more fundamental qualities is striking evidence of the general importance of inherited factors in determining a child's growth and development under ordinary environmental conditions; particularly as most of this resemblance is still found where the twins have been separated in infancy and brought up by different foster-parents.

The value of twins for genetic studies was indicated first by Francis Galton, born 1822, a versatile genius and a cousin of Charles Darwin (see Figure 46, p. 138). Galton was familiar with the idea that there are two types of twins, one type in which each twin is the product of a separate female germ cell or egg, and the other type in which both are derived from the same egg. In the latter case the twins were always of the same sex and he thought the twins always had a common afterbirth, that is a common chorionic membrane. He collected information by sending out a questionnaire to a number of twins and their relatives, asking for their life histories. He reported the findings first in 1875 in *Frazer's Magazine* and the *Anthropological Journal*, then in his book *Inquiries into Human Faculty* published in 1883.

Galton noted that many twins of the same sex, presumably those among them that were derived from a single ovum, were alike from birth and remained alike. This was especially marked for qualities such as eye-colour and hair-colour, and to a lesser degree for qualities such as height, weight, and temperament. He noted with height that sometimes twin A would start taller than B, then for a time B would lead, but finally their full adult heights were usually very much alike. With respect to temperament in these twins, Galton considered that the differences seen, when marked, were of intensity or energy and did not extend more deeply into the structure of the personality. Galton noted, too, that it was not uncommon for similar twins to experience the same illnesses. Sometimes these represented the late appearance of conditions which were inherited at birth, though dormant in early life, such as gout. Twins of unlike sex, however, and a proportion of like-sex twins, were often most unlike each other in early childhood and remained unlike in spite of being brought up and educated together.

*Identical and fraternal twins and the proportions of each type*

Since Galton's day the existence of two types of twins has been fully confirmed and a considerable advance made in diagnosing the type of twinning. The pairs derived from a single fertilized egg, or zygote, are most accurately described as *monozygotic* (sometimes abbreviated to *MZ*). This term emphasizes that they are derived from the same sperm as well as the same egg. They are commonly called '*identical*', and this is the term we shall use for them, but they are not exactly alike except for their inheritance. Identical twinning appears to be a freak of nature and the frequency of this type of twinning seems to be fairly constant – between three and four births in a thousand. It is much the same in different races and in different countries, and is more or less independent of the mother's age. This type of twinning shows no tendency to run in families.

The quite distinct type of twinning, in which the pair are derived from two fertilized eggs, or zygotes, is most accurately described as *dizygotic* (sometimes abbreviated to *DZ*). They are commonly called '*fraternal*'. The frequency of fraternal twinning shows interesting variations. It is much commoner in Europe than in Japan, where two-thirds of the twins are identical. It becomes increasingly common as mothers get older, rising to a maximum in mothers between thirty-five and thirty-nine and then falling in mothers over forty. In addition this type of twinning shows a marked tendency to run in families. The frequency of the two types of twinning in relation to mother's age is shown in Figure 1.

When the diagnosis of the type of twinning was based on whether there were one or two chorionic membranes in the afterbirth, it was considered that the proportion of twin births which were of identical twins in European countries was between 12 per cent and 15 per cent. But as early as 1874 the French mathematician, Bertillon, suggested that it should be possible to find out what proportion of twins were identical by examining the proportion of twins who were of like sex and of unlike sex. Identical twins must always be of the same sex; half of all fraternal twins are also of like sex. So the number of identical twins in any sample may be found by subtracting the unlike sex twins plus an equal number of like sex twins from the whole. In addition, a small allowance must be made for the fact that rather more boys than girls are born. By this method over a quarter of all twin pairs in western Europe would be identical, instead of only 12–15 per cent. In

1902, Weinberg, a German physician, reaffirmed the validity of this method. He noted, for example, that from the statistics of Prussia between 1826 and 1896, the percentage of unlike

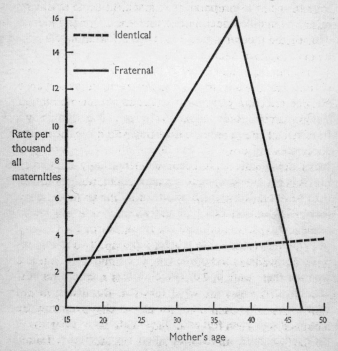

**1.** Twin births according to mother's age (England and Wales 1951–6)

sex twins was 37·3. The estimated percentage of fraternal twins was, therefore, 74·6 and identical twins 25·4.

The discrepancy between the estimates made from the afterbirths and from the sex ratio of twins was explained by two German doctors, Curtius and Verschuer. They showed that it was possible for identical twins each to have a separate chorion. This is understandable, since a chorion is formed by the embryo, and if an embryo splits sufficiently early in its development, then each resulting identical twin will form its own chorion. Nowadays, the proportion of identical twins calculated by Weinberg's method is found to correspond very well with the proportion estimated to be identical by modern methods of determining the type of twinning. It is now accepted that when twins each have a separate chorion they may be either identical or fraternal, though the majority will be fraternal. When twins share a chorion they are identical, but it is not uncommon for fraternal twins whose placentae are closely adherent to appear to have only one chorion. Careful study will show, however, that there are always two chorions in fraternal twins, and it is exceedingly rare for these to fuse.

Modern methods of determining the type of twinning were first developed by the German physician Siemens in the early 1920s. They consist essentially of testing the twin pair for a series of characteristics which are known to be genetically determined, and assigning the pairs which differ on any of these characteristics to the fraternal group. Those that remain are considered to be identical. It is impossible to prove positively that twins are identical by this method, but the probability that they are so increases as the twin pair are found to resemble each other for all the characteristics for which, had they been fraternal, they might have differed.

In the first place, all twins of unlike sex are clearly fraternal. Appreciable differences in hair-colour and form, or eye-colour, or shape of nose, or shape of hands, or shape of fingernails, all indicate that the twins are fraternal. Most reliable, however, are the blood groups when tested by an expert (see Chapter 4). There are now many different blood-group systems which may be tested, and if twins differ in any of these blood groups they are fraternal. With a knowledge of the blood groups of the parents it is possible to calculate the odds against the twins being the same for all the blood groups purely by chance. Very often, in practice, it is possible to build up a strong case against the twins being fraternal on the blood groups alone.

Finger-prints are also used. Galton was also the first to draw attention to the value of finger-prints in identification, and now it is well established that no two individuals have the same finger prints. Identical twins, however, are usually alike in their prints, so much so that it is not uncommon for, say, the left hand of one twin to be more like one hand of the other twin than his or her own right hand. Accordingly, the greater the differences in the finger-prints of a pair of twins, the greater the odds against their being identical.

*The use of twins in assessing the amount of hereditary variation*

The modern argument for the use of twins in the study of hereditary variation is as follows:

(1) for characteristics in which differences between one person and another are largely due to genetic variation, the resemblance of the identical twin pair will be nearly complete. But the resemblance of fraternal pairs will be considerably less since fraternal twins, like ordinary brothers and sisters, have only half their chromosomes (the structures which carry hereditary factors), on the average, in common.

(2) for characteristics in which differences between one person and another are largely due to their own environmental experience, the greater genetic resemblance of identical twins is unimportant and they will resemble each other no more than do fraternal twins.

(3) for the third group of characteristics in which differences may be due to both genetic and environmental differences, the resemblance of identical twins will be incomplete (according to the different experiences they have had), but still notably more than that of fraternal twins.

A recent study of the causes of congenital club foot provides an illustration of the use of twin studies. Babies with club foot are born with one or both feet turned in at the ankle. The deformity may be corrected by careful splinting in infancy and early childhood. In 1939 Idelberger, a German doctor, by patiently comparing the list of children attending orthopaedic clinics with birth registers, collected a large series of children with club foot who were the product of a twin birth. He then traced these children and also their twins. Sometimes of course, the other twin was dead, but where it was living Idelberger examined the child for the presence of club foot and also compared the two twins to see if they were identical or fraternal. He was not able to use blood groups, but mistakes in deciding the type of twinning are likely to have been few. His findings were clear-cut. Of 35 identical twins of his index cases 8, that is about 23 per cent, also had club foot. Of 65 like-sex fraternal pairs 1, that is only about 2 per cent, also had club foot. He was able to conclude that club foot fell into the group where both genetic and environmental factors were important in causation; genetic factors because the resemblance between the identical pairs was higher than that of the fraternal pairs; environmental factors because the resemblance of his identical pairs was incomplete. There is no certain knowledge of the environmental factor or factors which are important in club foot. It is presumably something which can affect one twin and not another, and a plausible suggestion is that it is pressure from the wall of the mother's womb on the feet of the embryo.

The same method can be used to test the importance of genetic factors in illnesses where the main cause is known to be environmental. Tuberculosis for example is primarily due to infection with the tubercle bacillus. The majority of men and women in this country are infected by the tubercle bacillus sooner or later in their lives. But the course the infection takes varies greatly. In some it leads to a generalized blood-borne disease, with death from damage to tissues all over the body. In some it leads to considerable but slowly progressive damage to the lungs alone. In some it leads to only a small amount of damage in the lungs or elsewhere, which is sealed off and causes no further trouble. Numerous intermediate forms are seen as well. This variation certainly depends to some extent on the age at which the man or woman is infected and on environmental conditions – tuberculosis was rife in the concentration camps in the Second World War – but there is also evidence that genetic factors play a part. Surveys in Germany, America, and most recently in this country have shown that if one twin has active tuberculosis of the lungs the other twin is more likely to have similar tuberculosis if identical than if fraternal.

The most sophisticated of these surveys on tuberculosis is one recently made in England. Here Simonds at first found, when she asked the staffs of chest clinics to let her know of all the new patients attending who were one of a twin pair, that she was getting too few twins and that the twins that were being reported to her were unrepresentative. They included too many identical pairs and too many pairs where both twins were affected. She was, however, able to get an unbiased sample by writing herself to all the patients of the clinics asking them whether they had a twin or not. Investigation of this group showed that of the identical co-twins 16 in 54, that is about 30 per cent, were also affected; while of the fraternal co-twins 19 in 148, that is 13 per cent, were also affected. These percentages were lower than for the other surveys, but resembled them in that the identical twins were significantly more often also affected than the fraternal twins. Even allowing for the fact that identical twins tend to go about more together, this finding suggests that genetic factors are important in a man's or a woman's resistance to infection by the tubercle bacillus.

*Twin studies of qualities showing continuous variation*

Surveys of twins may also be used to study qualities where

there is no division between normal and abnormal, but a continuously graded variation among normal people. Qualities of this kind are weight, height, and intelligence-test score. While there are individuals who are extremely short and others who are extremely tall, very often because of some disease or malformation affecting the skeleton, the great mass of ordinary adult Englishmen range between a height of 60 inches and 75 inches, with the average between 67 and 68 inches. In making comparisons between identical and fraternal twin pairs for characteristics of this kind, one cannot say a certain proportion of twins are also affected, but one can measure in various ways the resemblance of each type of twin.

Three scientists on the staff of the University of Chicago, Newman, Freeman, and Holzinger, made the most important of all twin studies for characteristics showing normal variation. They published their results in 1947. Part of their study was of 50 pairs judged to be identical and 52 pairs of the same sex judged to be fraternal, together with 52 non-twin brother and sister pairs. They expressed the resemblances between their twin pairs for height in two ways. Firstly, by the average difference between the twins; this was two-thirds of an inch (0·67) for the identical pairs, and a little over one and a half inches (1·73) for the fraternal pairs of the same sex. The difference for the fraternal pairs was very close to the figure they found for non-twin pairs of brothers and pairs of sisters (1·77 inches). Secondly, by the correlation coefficients* between the two types of twins; for the

---

* The correlation coefficient is a measure of the degree to which both members of a pair resemble each other in their deviation from the average of the series. A correlation coefficient may vary from +1, which would imply that the deviations in each member of the pair were in the same direction and of the same relative amount, through 0, which would imply no correspondence between members of the pair, and −1, which would imply correspondence in the amount of deviation, but in opposite directions.

identical pairs the correlation, when corrected for age, was $+0.93$ for the fraternal pairs $+0.65$, and for non-twin pairs of brothers and sisters $+0.60$. For unrelated pairs of individuals the correlation coefficient would be 0, and so the correlation coefficients indicate a strong likeness for all three types of pairs, but it is much higher for the identical pairs than for the others. These findings for height differences in twins strongly suggest that genetic factors are important for height. The same type of comparisons may be used for other characteristics, such as weight, intelligence-test score, blood-pressure, and longevity.

### Identical twins reared apart

In addition to the twin pairs reared together, Newman and his colleagues managed to assemble 19 pairs of identical twins who, because they were orphans, had been adopted and adopted into different homes. In many instances these were most valuable in providing examples of men and women with the same heredity, who had been brought up in contrasting environments. Sometimes the contrast was in education and social class, sometimes between town and country. In two pairs the twins had even been reared in different countries. One of each pair had been brought up in Canada, while the other twin of one pair was reared in America and of the other pair in England.

The differences in height between these identical twins reared apart were little more than that for identical twins reared together, and it may reasonably be concluded that the environmental differences experienced had little influence on their height. It should be added that most of these 19 pairs were fully grown. Within the twin pairs there was no tendency for the twins who had social, educational, or physical and health advantages to be the taller of the pair. There is good reason from other lines of evidence also to suppose that full adult height belongs to the group of characteristics in which men and women differ, except in very exceptional circumstances, mainly because of genetic differences and not environmental ones (see Chapter 6). In contrast to stature, weight in the Chicago study was found to be much more dependent on environmental factors. The correlation coefficient for the identical twin pairs reared together was high, $+0.92$, when corrected for age, and that for fraternal twin pairs reared together was $+0.63$, corrected for age. This indicates a strong genetic component in the determination of weight. The resemblance of the identical twins reared apart, however, was notably less, and within the twin pairs the twin with social advantages and even more the twin with physical and health advantages was the heavier.

Table 1 shows correlations, corrected for age, for the 50 identical and 50 fraternal pairs reared together, for height, weight, two intelligence tests, educational achievement, and a motor character, the speed at which they could tap. These

Table 1. Twin correlations

|  | Identical | Fraternal |
| --- | --- | --- |
| Standing height | $+0.93$ | $+0.65$ |
| Weight | $+0.92$ | $+0.63$ |
| Binet intelligence-test score | $+0.86$ | $+0.60$ |
| Otis intelligence-test score | $+0.92$ | $+0.62$ |
| Educational age | $+0.89$ | $+0.70$ |
| Tapping speed | $+0.69$ | $+0.38$ |

figures indicate a strong genetic element in the determination of each of these qualities, except for educational age.

## Difficulties in the interpretation of twin studies

In theory, there are a number of difficulties which reduce the value of the twin method in determining the extent to which hereditary factors are important in the development of a particular characteristic or quality. One factor acting after birth is that identical twins tend to go about more together than fraternal twins and so are more liable to the same environmental experiences. This will cause identical twins to resemble each other more than fraternal twins for non-genetic reasons. For most qualities this factor is not likely to be important, but it should be borne in mind.

A possible factor acting before birth is that the communications between the blood streams of those identical twin pairs who have a common chorionic membrane might lead to one twin's circulation interfering with that of the other. The observations on which this suggestion is based were made at the end of the last century and an interesting study now begun in Toronto will provide new information on its importance. In the study the afterbirths of twins are being examined and kept. The twins are being studied and it will be possible to see if, and in what ways, identical twins with a common chorion differ more than do identical twins with separate chorions. There are indications that inadequate blood supply to a foetus may have long lasting effects on development, and this mechanism might account for occasional instances where one member of an identical twin pair is markedly smaller and less intelligent than the other.

A third factor, an interesting one, is that some degree of differentiation into left- and right-handedness may have occurred in identical twins before they separate. It was observed early in twin studies that left-handedness is unusually common among twins. There has been some disagreement whether this is true of both types of twins or only identical twins, but it is probably more marked for the latter. In the Chicago series 39 of the 50 fraternal pairs were both right-handed, but only 30 of the 50 identical pairs were both right-handed. This is not a significant difference by itself, but is in general agreement with the findings in other series. Similar evidence of asymmetry occurs in the direction of the hair whorl at the back of the top of the head, which is usually clockwise. In the Chicago series 44 of 49 fraternal pairs both had a clockwise whorl, but only 27 of 47 identical pairs. Similar asymmetry has been observed in the finger and palm prints of identical pairs. It is noteworthy that these asymmetries are usually partial, and identical twin pairs who differ for hand dominance do not necessarily differ for direction of hair whorl. Asymmetries are specially marked in identical twins who have never separated completely, so-called Siamese twins, and these twins show differences unusually large for identical twins in their general development. Asymmetry as a cause of difference is probably not important except for the qualities it affects directly such as hand and eye dominance.

It will be noted that the two pre-natal factors mentioned will tend to reduce, and the post-natal factor will tend to increase the resemblance of identical pairs. But at the moment there is no reason to suppose that any of these factors interferes with the use of the twin comparison method in general, for determining whether there is an important genetic component for the development of a characteristic. They may be important in the study of individual characteristics.

What promises to be the most thorough of all large-scale twin studies has now been started in Denmark at the Institute of Human Genetics in Copenhagen, with the object of tracing every twin born there between the years 1870 and 1910 and studying the illnesses they have experienced.

Twin studies, however, are only a first approach to understanding the hereditary factors which influence the development of a quality. They tell whether inherited factors are important or not, but little about the nature of the factors involved. To study the nature of the inherited factors it is necessary to study the resemblances and differences within families, between parent and child, brothers and sisters, and between other relatives.

Anyone who, like the author, studies twins in the course of his work is left with the strong impression of the general importance of genetic factors in controlling a child's development.

# CHAPTER 2

# Genes and Chromosomes

THE first scientist to put forward a satisfactory theory of the mechanism of inheritance was an Austrian monk, Gregor Mendel, of the Abbey of Brunn. He experimented with peas during the seven years from 1856 to 1863 in a strip of the monastery garden and published his work in 1866 in the *Proceedings of the Brunn Society for the Study of Natural Science*. The value of his discoveries was not recognized at the time. Mendel discontinued his experiments and became head of the monastery. Only years after his death did scientists realize that Mendel should be regarded, with Galton, as one of the founders of the science of Genetics.

## Genes are in pairs

Mendel's general findings may be illustrated from those for the height of pea plants. He found that a hybrid between a true-breeding tall strain and a true-breeding short strain was always a tall offspring; but that if two of these tall hybrids were self-fertilized or crossed with each other one in four of the offspring, on the average, was short. He postulated that the tall strain had two hereditary factors for tallness, *TT*, and the short strain two hereditary factors for shortness, *tt*; that the hybrids received one hereditary factor from each parent and had the genetic constitution *Tt*; and that such a pea with one hereditary factor for tallness *T* and one for shortness *t* was as tall as one with the genetic constitution *TT*. He postulated further that, when a plant forms germ cells, only one member of the pair of factors for height passes into the germ cell and that it is pure chance which it is. Thus, a hybrid tall pea, with genetic constitution *Tt*, is equally likely to form germ cells with the factor for tallness $T$, or the factor for shortness $t$. (Hereditary factors are now commonly called *genes* and the combination of genes that an individual plant or animal possesses is called its *genotype*.) The possible genotypes in the offspring of $Tt$ plants, when self-fertilized, and the proportions in which they will be expected to occur, are as in Figures 2a and 2b. Figure 2a shows the transmission and recombination of the genes. Figure 2b shows how the types of offspring can conveniently be worked out from the types of germ cells by a chequer-board diagram.

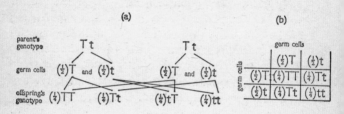

2. Mendel's derivation of genotypes from germ cells

The peas with genotype $Tt$ as well as those with genotype $TT$ are tall and so the offspring of the self-fertilized $Tt$ plant are $\frac{3}{4}$ tall and $\frac{1}{4}$ short. With small numbers in a particular experiment the proportions of each type might well differ from this, but with large numbers they would be most un-likely to differ much; just as when one tosses two pennies many times the combinations of two heads, one head and one tail, and two tails, are usually close to the proportion of $\frac{1}{4} : \frac{1}{2} : \frac{1}{4}$. The frequency of departures from the expected proportion of one in four short plants may easily be calcu-lated for any given number of observations by standard statistical procedures. For example, in the case of an ex-periment in which there were 1,000 offspring, the expected number of short plants is 250, and it can be shown that in only about one batch in 20 will the number of short peas deviate from 250 by more than 28. In one of Mendel's experiments there were 277 short plants out of a total of 1,064, which is only 11 away from the theoretical expectation, $\frac{1}{4}$ of 1,064, which is 266.

Mendel then proceeded to self-fertilize the short and tall plants, which were the offspring of his first generation crosses, and so produced a third generation. He found, as would be expected on his theory, that the short plants, all having genotype $tt$, when self-fertilized produced only short offspring: that about $\frac{1}{3}$ of the tall plants, those with genotype $TT$, produced only tall offspring; and that the other $\frac{2}{3}$ of the tall plants, those with genotype $Tt$, produced tall and short offspring in the proportions $\frac{3}{4}$ and $\frac{1}{4}$.

## Independent segregation of gene pairs

Mendel further noted that in crosses between peas differing in several characters, each controlled by a single gene pair, each gene pair segregated independently of the others. Thus, taking peas contrasting in two characteristics, a yellow, round-seeded strain with genetic constitution $YYRR$, and a green, wrinkled-seeded strain with genetic constitution $yyrr$, he crossed them to produce hybrids which were yellow and round-seeded, and genetically $YyRr$. On self-fertilizing these hybrids he found that the offspring were $\frac{9}{16}$ yellow round, $\frac{3}{16}$ yellow wrinkled, $\frac{3}{16}$ green round, and $\frac{1}{16}$ green wrinkled. Mendel suggested that this showed that the segregation of the $Y$ and $y$ genes was independent of the segregation of the $R$ and $r$ genes. Four types of germ cells were formed $YR$, $Yr$, $yR$ and $yr$, each with a probability of $\frac{1}{4}$. The chequer-board Figure 3 shows how Mendel's theory explains the proportions of each type. It should be remembered that $Yy$ as well as $YY$ peas are yellow and $Rr$ as well as $RR$ peas are round.

Mendel deliberately chose for study characteristics which

|  | $(\frac{1}{4})$ YR | $(\frac{1}{4})$ Yr | $(\frac{1}{4})$ yR | $(\frac{1}{4})$ yr |
|---|---|---|---|---|
| $(\frac{1}{4})$ YR | $(\frac{1}{16})\dfrac{YR}{YR}$ yellow round | $(\frac{1}{16})\dfrac{Yr}{YR}$ yellow round | $(\frac{1}{16})\dfrac{yR}{YR}$ yellow round | $(\frac{1}{16})\dfrac{yr}{YR}$ yellow round |
| $(\frac{1}{4})$ Yr | $(\frac{1}{16})\dfrac{YR}{Yr}$ yellow round | $(\frac{1}{16})\dfrac{Yr}{Yr}$ yellow wrinkled | $(\frac{1}{16})\dfrac{yR}{Yr}$ yellow round | $(\frac{1}{16})\dfrac{yr}{Yr}$ yellow wrinkled |
| $(\frac{1}{4})$ yR | $(\frac{1}{16})\dfrac{YR}{yR}$ yellow round | $(\frac{1}{16})\dfrac{Yr}{yR}$ yellow round | $(\frac{1}{16})\dfrac{yR}{yR}$ green round | $(\frac{1}{16})\dfrac{yr}{yR}$ green round |
| $(\frac{1}{4})$ yr | $(\frac{1}{16})\dfrac{YR}{yr}$ yellow round | $(\frac{1}{16})\dfrac{Yr}{yr}$ yellow wrinkled | $(\frac{1}{16})\dfrac{yR}{yr}$ green round | $(\frac{1}{16})\dfrac{yr}{yr}$ green wrinkled |

3. Mendel's theory that the genes for seed colour in hybrid peas are inherited quite separately from the genes for seed shape

depended essentially on a single gene pair. But it is interesting that he gave the correct explanation for instances where inheritance appears more complex, as with flower colours in the garden bean. He suggested that in these instances, there were several gene pairs controlling the development of the characteristic and that it was not yet possible to recognize the influence of single gene pairs. Perhaps it was because it so often happens that a characteristic is influenced by several gene pairs that the value of Mendel's hypothesis was not appreciated at the time.

*Mendel's work rediscovered*

In papers published in 1900, three botanists, De Vries of Holland, Correns of Germany, and Tschermak of Austria, independently confirmed Mendel's findings on peas and other plants and, during the course of their work, discovered that Mendel had preceded them by more than thirty years. It is perhaps remarkable that none of the medical profession had appreciated Mendel's work. A number of pedigrees of rare human disorders had already been published showing patterns of heredity, which are at once explicable on Mendel's theory of the nature of inheritance. The physicians however, unlike Mendel, had formulated no general theory of inheritance.

## The mechanism of inheritance – chromosomes

The material basis of Mendelian inheritance was discovered by expert use of the microscope between the time of Mendel's own work and its rediscovery in 1900. The cells of living organisms, with a few exceptions, consist of an outer membrane enclosing a mass of jelly-like material known as 'cytoplasm', with a darker-staining structure within the cytoplasm known as the 'nucleus'. The outer cell membrane separates one cell from another, and within the cell a nuclear membrane separates the contents of the nucleus from the cytoplasm. The structures concerned with inheritance lie largely within the nucleus. This is shown by the finding, noted by Mendel, that the male contribution to inheritance is as great as the female, although the sperm cell is composed almost entirely of nucleus while the egg cell contains much cytoplasm as well as nucleus. In addition, in animals such as the sea urchin, it is possible to fertilize an egg cell from which the nucleus has been removed, with the sperm cell of another species. In these experiments it was found that development is towards the form contributing the sperm cell and nucleus, rather than the form contributing the egg cell and cytoplasm.

Within the nucleus, darker-staining material, known as 'chromatin', is visible as fine, tangled threads; but before the cell divides the chromatin contracts into a number of bodies known as 'chromosomes'. The number of these chromosomes is constant for each species. Early counts in man gave a figure of 48 chromosomes, and this is the number in man's near relatives, the gorilla, chimpanzee, and orang-utan, but in 1956 a Javanese, Tjio, and his Swedish colleague, Levan, showed that there were 46. This was confirmed by two British workers, Ford and Hamerton, from the Atomic Energy Research Establishment at Harwell. A photograph of the human chromosomes is shown in Plate 2a.

In 1902 the American, Sutton, and the German, Boveri, pointed out independently that the behaviour of the chromosomes in germ-cell formation and fertilization very closely fitted Mendel's principles of inheritance. Cells divide in the course of bodily growth and development, but the nucleus divides in two before the cell divides. Before this nuclear division each chromosome in the nucleus divides longitudinally and one half passes into each division of the nucleus and so into each daughter cell. Each of the two new cells contains a nucleus with a full complement of chromosomes, 46 in human beings. But when germ cells are formed the process differs. Here there are two divisions of the nuclei of the germ-forming cells, but only one division of the chromosomes, so that the sperm cell and egg cell each contain only 23 chromosomes. In sperm-cell formation the cytoplasm divides as well as the nucleus so that four sperms are formed. In egg-cell formation the cytoplasm does not divide and all but one of the daughter nuclei are extruded. The differences between ordinary body-cell and germ-cell formation are illustrated in Figure 4 for a single pair of chromosomes.

The reduction of the number of chromosomes in germ-cell formation is orderly and regular, in that the 23 chromosomes in a human sperm cell (or egg cell) include one, and it is pure chance which one, from each of the pairs of chromosomes present in the man or woman forming the

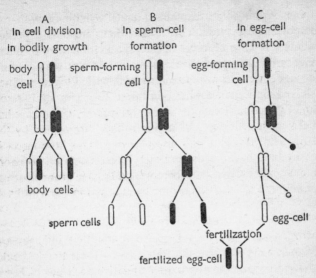

A
In cell division
in bodily growth

B
In sperm-cell
formation

C
In egg-cell
formation

body cell

sperm-forming cell

egg-forming cell

body cells

sperm cells

egg-cell

fertilization

fertilized egg-cell

4. The behaviour of a single chromosome pair in cell division

germ cell. Upon fertilization, which consists of the entry of the sperm into the egg cell and the fusion of the two nuclei, a fertilized cell is formed, known as a 'zygote', which once more has 46 chromosomes. These consist of 23 pairs, one of each pair being derived from the male parent through the sperm and the other from the female parent through the egg cell. This zygote then grows by cell division to form first the embryo, then the infant, the child, and ultimately the adult. In each of these cell divisions the daughter cells receive the full complement of 46 chromosomes. When the child grows into an adult and itself forms germ cells, these once again contain only 23 unpaired chromosomes.

*Linkage between genes on the same chromosome*

As Sutton noted, if one assumes that the hereditary factors (or 'genes') lie on the chromosomes, the behaviour of these chromosomes explains Mendel's findings, with one important exception. This is that there are only a limited number of chromosomes in each species of animal or plant. Genes on the same chromosome would not segregate independently, but would tend to be inherited together. Such 'linked' inheritance was soon found to occur, by Bateson and Punnett in sweet peas at Cambridge in 1905. Linkage has been most fully studied in the fruitfly, *Drosophila*, by the American, Morgan, and his colleagues. This little insect is easily bred and breeds very fast. Experiments on an enormous scale showed that there were 4 linkage groups corresponding to the 4 chromosome pairs found in the fruitfly.

## Mapping the position of genes on the chromosomes

Morgan and his colleagues also found that linkages are often broken and that the frequency of these breaks could be used to map the approximate relative positions of genes on the chromosomes. The physical basis for these breaks in linkage is that in the process of germ-cell formation the two adjoining halves of the two members of a chromosome pair twine round each other and may exchange segments. This process, known as 'crossing-over', may separate genes in the exchanged segment from the remainder, as illustrated in Figure 5.

Genes which are situated close together on the same chromosome, like $Y$ and $Z$ in the diagram, will seldom be separated by crossing-over; usually either both or neither will be in the exchanged segment.

Systematic studies of cross-over frequencies between linked genes in the fruitfly enabled Morgan and his colleagues to build up detailed maps of the relative positions of the genes on each of the 4 chromosome pairs, and whenever a new gene is discovered in this insect it is possible quickly to find its position relative to other genes on the same chromosome pair. In recent years some interesting direct confirmation of the gene maps in the fruitfly has come from experimentally fragmenting chromosomes with large doses of X-rays to the germ cells. In this way portions of chromosomes may become lost, and, where the offspring live and develop, the effect of the missing genes may be seen.

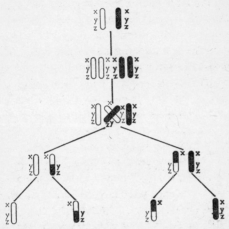

5. The way in which genes originally on the same chromosome may be separated by 'crossing-over' during germ-cell formation

*Linkage in Man*

In human beings, with 23 chromosome pairs and the long interval between generations, the search for linkage is inevitably slow. The first probable linkage other than for genes on the sex chromosomes was reported by Mohr of Norway in 1951 between two of the many genes controlling the blood groups, the two called *Lewis* and *Lutheran*. Two certain examples have been discovered recently by Lawler and her colleagues in England of linkage between two physical abnormalities and blood-group genes. In one case the physical abnormality is an oval shape of the red blood cells

(illustrated in Plate 1b) and the linkage is with the genes
responsible for the Rhesus series of blood types (see Chapter
4 for an account of the Rhesus types). One of these families
is illustrated in Figure 6 and it will be seen that in this family
all those with oval red cells (shown as ■ or ● in the diagram)
who were blood-grouped also have the gene for the blood-
group substance $R_2$, often called CDE (see Chapter 4).
In family trees such as Figure 6, it is usual to block in the
symbols for those who are affected and to refer to individuals by their generation and number from the left, for example the affected girl at the left-hand bottom corner of the
pedigree is III 1.

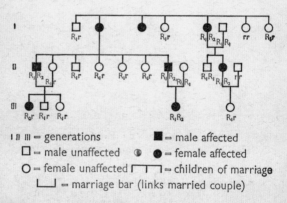

I II III = generations        ■ = male affected
    □ = male unaffected    ● = female affected
    O = female unaffected  ⌐⌐ = children of marriage
        ⌐ = marriage bar (links married couple)

6. Part of one of Goodall, Hendry, Lawler, and Stephen's
families with oval red blood cells

In the other example the abnormality affects the nails and
kneecaps, and the linkage is with the genes controlling the
ABO blood groups (for which see Chapter 4). One of these
families is illustrated in Figure 7; it shows that those who
have the nail and knee abnormality (shown as ■ or ●) also
have the gene for the blood substance B.

There are no cross-overs in the two families illustrated, but crossing-over does occur in other families, and provisional estimates of cross-over values are now being made for these two linkages. These will become more precise as more families are found with these abnormalities. It is important to note that linkage is primarily between the position of

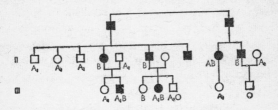

A, B, and O = A B O blood group substance

7. Part of one of Renwick and Lawler's families with abnormalities of the nails and kneecaps

genes on the chromosomes, called 'gene-loci', and not between genes. In the second family illustrated above (Figure 7) the gene for the abnormality of nails and kneecaps segregates with the gene for blood-group substance B. In other families in which the abnormality occurs, the linkage is with one of the alternative genes at the ABO gene-locus. A particular blood-group substance and the abnormality occur in association within a family; but a cross-over will alter the future association within that family, and there is no correspondence between different families. An association between two characteristics in the general population should not be attributed to linkage; only an association within individual families can be caused by linkage.

In time it will be possible to draw up maps showing the positions of genes on the human chromosomes, but these will not be complete for at least a century and perhaps much longer.

*Common terms*

It is convenient here to introduce, or to remind readers of, some terms which will be used in the rest of the book.

An individual's genetic constitution is called his genotype. His actual appearance, which is the product of his genotype and the environment he has experienced, is called his 'phenotype'. The site of a gene on a chromosome is called a gene-locus. Alternative forms of a gene, which may occur at a single gene-locus, are called 'allelomorphs' or 'alleles'. An individual animal or plant with the same allele on each member of the chromosome pair, for example a pea with genes for height $T$ and $T$, is said to be 'homozygous' for this gene-locus, the corresponding noun being 'homozygote'. In contrast an individual with two different alleles at the corresponding gene-locus of the chromosome pair is said to be 'heterozygous' for that gene-locus or a 'heterozygote'. Where the phenotype of the heterozygote cannot be distinguished from that of one of the two homozygotes, as with height in the pea, where the plant with the genotype $Tt$ is as tall as the plant with the genotype $TT$, then the allele $T$ is said to be 'dominant' to $t$, and $t$ to be 'recessive' to $T$.

In proposing symbols for genes it has become the practice in recent years to use a symbol with a capital letter for the gene locus and a small superscript to distinguish the allele, for example $Le^a$ and $Le^b$ for the two producing the Lewis substances in the red blood cells.

*How genes function*

A remarkable amount, especially in the last decade, has been discovered about the ways in which genes carry out their functions by scientists studying the genetics of microorganisms, such as bacteria and viruses. The first step, however, was taken by an English physician, Garrod, who in 1908 gave a series of lectures, *Inborn Errors of Metabolism*, in which he described a number of illnesses in children which behaved as if they were due to Mendelian recessive genes. Each of these conditions appeared to be due to an inborn incapacity of the body to carry out one of the normal chemical processes. It is known that many chemical processes in living tissues do not take place, or only take place slowly, unless a special chemical compound is present, which greatly accelerates the reaction. These accelerating substances are known as 'enzymes' and chemically they are proteins. Garrod's concept was that specific enzymes were missing in the conditions studied and that as a result of the enzyme-lack certain chemicals, which normally would have undergone further change, accumulated in the tissues, then in the blood, and finally spilled over into the urine. In 1941 the Americans Beadle and Tatum, working with fungi, formulated more precisely this concept of 'one gene – one enzyme'.

It was the spilling over of blocked chemicals into the urine which enabled them to be picked up in Garrod's day; but now the technique of examining the chemistry of the blood and also of staining cells themselves to show their chemical constituents is much advanced. Some illnesses are known in which the enzyme-lack can be shown to lead to the accumulation of a chemical within the cells of a tissue, with perhaps little rise in the level of the substance in the blood and no spill over into the urine. It will probably prove to be an over-simplification to say that each gene is responsible for the production of one particular protein, often an enzyme, but it is a useful approximation to the truth.

One of Garrod's examples is a rare condition known as alcaptonuria, which is due to a recessive gene. In men and women with this abnormality the urine turns black on standing, due to the presence of a chemical known as homogentisic acid which is gradually changed by the presence of oxygen in the air to a black compound. Homogentisic acid is, Garrod suggested, a normal stage in the breakdown of two of the aminoacid constituents of protein-containing foods, phenylalanine and tyrosine. Phenylalanine found in meat and other protein food is formed into tyrosine and then this tyrosine, together with directly ingested tyrosine in excess of the body's needs, is converted to homogentisic acid. Most men and women can break down homogentisic acid to carbon dioxide and water and even if they are fed with large amounts of phenylalanine or tyrosine none appears in the urine. Alcaptonuric men and women, however, excrete most of a large dose of either of these two aminoacids as homogentisic acid, and Garrod suggested that they lacked the enzyme responsible for breaking down homogentisic acid. An alternative explanation was considered: that the essential abnormality in affected men and women is in the kidneys – that these rapidly excrete any homogentisic acid present in the blood plasma so that no further breakdown can occur; however the enzyme deficiency has now been demonstrated. Apart from the urine turning black there are no signs of this disease in childhood, but later in life the teeth and the cartileges of the ear may be blackened, and osteoarthritis (joint inflammation due to degeneration of bone) may develop.

Another example of an inborn error of phenylalanine metabolism, barely known to Garrod, has been particularly well studied in man. The disorder causes mental deficiency, is known as phenylketonuria, and is due to a recessive gene. It was first recognized by a Norwegian doctor, Fölling, in 1934. The great majority of these patients have a level of mental performance normally found in children of only half their age or less. They may be distinguished from other mentally handicapped children by testing their urine. This gives a green colour reaction with a solution of ferric chloride, due to the presence of derivatives of phenylalanine. Children affected by phenylketonuria are not able to convert phenylalanine into tyrosine and are only able to break it down to a limited extent. Why this should produce mental deficiency is not certain, but probably some of the incomplete break-down products of phenylalanine are poisonous to the nervous system. Since very little phenylalanine is needed in the diet, provided the tyrosine is present, it is possible to feed these children on a diet almost free of phenylalanine. Numerous children are now being treated in this way, and provided that treatment is begun in the first few weeks of life mental retardation may be entirely prevented. There is no question here of the alternative explanation suggested for alcaptonuria, unusually rapid excretion by the kidney. The enzyme has been shown to be absent in pieces of liver tissue removed during operations on these patients, whereas pieces of normal liver tissue break down phenylalanine readily. The disease is relatively common in Ireland as well as Norway.

## Chemical nature of the gene

A mass of work since, on many different varieties of animals and plants, both large and small, has fully confirmed the concept that genes control the production of proteins and that often these proteins are enzymes which speed chemical processes in the cell. Genes, then, have two special properties: the ability to reproduce themselves and the ability to produce proteins. In recent years chemical analysis and X-ray study of chromosomes, mainly in the Cavendish laboratory at Cambridge, have given some insight into the chemical structure of chromosomes and the way in which this structure is related to self reproduction and protein function.

The basic chemical compound of which chromosomes, and therefore genes, are made is deoxyribonucleic acid (DNA for short) joined to protein. Studies in bacteria show that it is the DNA which has genetic specificity. DNA is made up of chemical units consisting of a base (such as adenine or guanine) and a sugar (deoxyribose), the units being linked to each other by phosphate as shown in Figure 8. There is, then, a sugar-phosphate backbone to which bases are attached.

```
Base——Sugar<
                 >Phosphate
Base——Sugar<
                 >Phosphate
Base——Sugar<
                 >Phosphate
```

8. Constituents of deoxy-
ribonucleic acid

There are four bases in DNA, called adenine, guanine,
cytosine and thymine. The proportion of each in the DNA of
any one species is constant, but varies from one species to
another. There is evidence that the DNA in chromosomes
is in the form of a double chain. The chains are wound round
each other in a helical formation and are attached by their
bases in much the same way as the continous sides of a spiral
staircase are connected by the stairs. Each base can only
attach itself to one of the other three bases. Adenine is always
opposite to and attached to thymine and guanine opposite to
and attached to cytosine as shown in Figure 9.

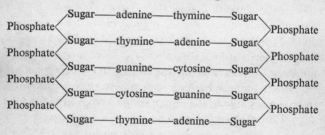

9. Structural formula of deoxyribonucleic acid

The way in which genes reproduce themselves is thought to
be that the two chains uncoil and separate. Each half attracts
to itself, from the surrounding medium, the units to recon-
stitute a complementary chain. Thus, a segment of DNA with

the sequence of bases adenine, thymine, guanine would attract a segment with bases thymine, adenine, cytosine.

The way in which DNA is able to produce enzymes and other proteins is probably less simple. Proteins are composed of chains of aminoacids in regular patterns analogous to that of DNA itself. Once again there is a constant grouping through which the aminoacids are linked and a component which will vary from one aminoacid to another. The constant grouping is the structure.

$$C \Big\langle \begin{array}{l} COOH \\ NH_2 \end{array}$$

in which C represents an atom of carbon, H an atom of hydrogen, N an atom of nitrogen, and O an atom of oyxgen. Two aminoacids join by the acidic COOH grouping of one combining with the basic $NH_2$ element of the other.

$$\text{Thus: } R_1 \quad C \Big\langle \begin{array}{l} NH_2 \\ COOH \end{array} \quad \text{and } R_2 - C \Big\langle \begin{array}{l} NH_2 \\ COOH \end{array}$$

$$\text{becomes} \quad \begin{array}{l} R_1 - C \Big\langle \begin{array}{l} NH_2 \\ CO \end{array} \\ R_2 - C \Big\langle \begin{array}{l} NH \\ COOH \end{array} \end{array}$$

In any one link in the chain there may be up to twenty components of the type we have shown as R. This pattern is not unlike that of DNA and it is understandable that DNA could act as the template on which enzymes and other proteins are formed. Most proteins, however, are not made in the nucleus but in permanent structures in the cytoplasm known as ribosomes. The necessary intermediary substance is a large 'messenger' molecule made up of ribose nucleic acid (RNA) which is formed by the activity of a length of DNA (a structural gene). The structure of RNA is very like that of

DNA, differing only in the sugar (ribose instead of deoxyribose) and the substitution of uracil for thymine as one of the four bases; the base sequence in a messenger RNA molecule will be complementary to that of the DNA which formed it and unlike the DNA strip is soluble. Once formed the messenger RNA passes to the ribosomes and there acts as a template. Individual aminoacids are present in the cytoplasm, already joined to short soluble RNA molecules. These aminoacid–RNA complexes are attracted to and juxtaposed on the messenger RNA template, so that the aminoacids join to form a protein. The messenger RNA forms several molecules of protein, then breaks up. A single ribosome can form many proteins under the influence of successive messenger molecules. The aminoacid sequence, and so the specificity of the protein, depends on the base sequence in the messenger RNA. This in turn was determined by the base sequence of the particular length of DNA which formed the messenger RNA.

## Breaking the genetic code

Late in 1961 Nirenberg and his colleagues from America reported that on adding a synthetic RNA, all of whose bases were uracil, to a system of broken-up bacterial cells, a protein precursor was formed made up of the single aminoacid phenylalanine. Early in 1962 Crick and his colleagues at the Cavendish laboratory reported evidence that the basic unit of DNA, which 'codes' one aminoacid, is a sequence of three of the four possible bases. They studied gene mutations in a virus which attacks the bacterium *Escherichia coli*. These mutations involve the addition or deletion of a single base. The addition of one base destroys the function of the gene; the addition of a second leaves the gene still functionless; but the addition of a third largely restores the function of the gene. This is understandable if the sequence is of three bases and if the sequence starts from a fixed point.

| | | | | |
|---|---|---|---|---|
| If the natural sequence is | 1 2 3 | 1 2 3 | 1 2 3 | .. .. |
| the effect of adding one base, which we will call A, is | A 1 2 | 3 1 2 | 3 1 2 | .. .. |
| the effect of adding a second base, which we will call B, is | A B 1 | 2 3 1 | 2 3 1 | .. .. |
| the effect of adding a third base, which we will call C, is | A B C | 1 2 3 | 1 2 3 | .. .. |

Thus the natural sequence 1 2 3 is re-established with the addition of the third base, and with it the function of the gene. It was apparent therefore, that a triplet of uracil bases in messenger RNA, hence a triplet of adenine bases (AAA) in DNA, was the genetic code for phenylalanine and that an AAA triplet at a particular place within a structural gene, caused the insertion of phenylalanine in the corresponding place in the protein produced by the gene. Using Nirenberg's techniques, the genetic code for each aminoacid had been largely worked out by 1965 and the concept of 'one gene – one enzyme' has been reduced to 'one triplet of bases – one aminoacid'. There are only twenty aminoacids found in proteins and there are sixty-four ways in which three bases may be chosen out of four alternatives. Therefore, some aminoacids must be codable by more than one triplet. It appears that the coding specificity often lies mainly in the first two bases while the third may vary. For example, both AAA and AAG triplets in DNA will code phenylalanine and both AGT and AGC will code the aminoacid serine.

These are exciting developments. The code appears to be much the same in all living organisms from viruses to man. Dreams of a direct attack on human DNA to correct genetic abnormalities no longer seem entirely impractical.

# CHAPTER 3

# The Sex Chromosomes

*A normal variation due to one pair of chromosomes*

NORMAL inherited differences between one person and another are due to differences in the genes which they possess. Such gene differences usually involve very small sections of a chromosome. The essential genetic difference between male and female, however, is a difference of a whole chromosome. Microscopists have no difficulty in grouping the 46 chromosomes in women into 23 matching pairs, the two members of each pair being very much alike in size and shape. In men 44 of the 46 chromosomes may be grouped in 22 matching pairs, leaving two chromosomes which bear no resemblance to each other. One is a large chromosome, known as the $X$ chromosome, closely resembling each of a pair of chromosomes in the female, which are about the seventh pair in descending order of size. The other is a very small chromosome, about the same size as the chromosomes of the two smallest pairs, and is known as the $Y$ chromosome. This is illustrated in Plate 2b. A woman, therefore, is said to have two $X$ chromosomes, and has the genotype $XX$, while a man has the genotype $XY$.

By a mechanism as yet unknown, the presence of an $XY$ pair leads, in early foetal life, to the differentiation of the primordial sex gland into a testis. This is followed by the development of the male sex organs and other male sex characters. The presence of an $XX$ pair, on the other hand, leads the primordial sex gland to develop into an ovary, and this is followed by the development of the female sex organs and other female sex characters. The $X$ and $Y$ chromosomes are called sex chromosomes, and the remaining chromosomes are called, in distinction, autosomes.

## The father's germ cell determines sex

The $XX$ and $XY$ chromosomes behave at germ-cell formation and fertilization like other pairs, and the sex of a child is determined essentially by whether the father transmits his $X$ or his $Y$ chromosome. The mother having two $X$ chromosomes, can only transmit an $X$ chromosome. This is represented in Figure 10.

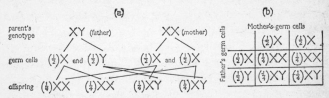

10. (a) Sex determination (b) Sex determination in chequer-board form

## Sex ratio

It will be seen that by this mechanism any child would have an even chance of being a boy or a girl. It is an unexplained puzzle that this is not quite what actually happens. There have been about 106 boys born alive for every 100 girls in recent years in England and Wales; the younger the parents, the greater the excess of boys. Among still-born children the male preponderance is even greater, in recent years about 110 boys to 100 girls; and study of foetuses lost by miscarriage suggests that a similar excess of boys is present at least from the third month of pregnancy. Since the death-rate in boys and men is higher than that in girls and women the male excess gradually disappears. The sexes are now numerically equal by about the age of thirty-three and by the age of seventy-five and over there are only 54 men to every 100 women.

*Sex linkage*

Because the $X$ chromosome is much larger than the $Y$ chromosome, for many genes on the $X$ chromosome there are no corresponding genes on the $Y$ chromosome. This leads to special patterns of inheritance, particularly with recessive genes. A woman with such a gene on one $X$ chromosome only will not be affected by it, just as individuals heterozygous for a recessive gene on one of the other chromosomes are unaffected. But a man or boy with such a gene on his $X$ chromosome will have no normal alternative gene on his $Y$ chromosome and will, therefore, be affected by it. Genes on the $X$ chromosome are called sex-linked.

A well-known example of a condition due to a sex-linked gene is haemophilia. There are many varieties of disorder of the clotting mechanism of the blood. One of these is classical haemophilia, sometimes called haemophilia A, in which one specific component of the protein in the liquid part of the blood, the blood plasma, is missing. The disease is normally found only in males, and if one asks about the family history, one not uncommonly finds that an uncle of the mother or a son of a sister of the mother is also affected. Less commonly, since haemophilia is a considerable handicap, and not many affected men have children, one finds that the mother's father was affected. A type of pedigree commonly found in haemophilia is shown in Figure 11 and alongside the pedigree are shown the corresponding sex chromosomes; the $X$ chromosome with the gene for haemophilia is marked with a bar over it.

Where a condition is due to a gene on the $X$ chromosome a man cannot transmit the condition to his son, since he transmits his $Y$ chromosome and not his $X$ chromosome to his son. If, for example, a haemophilic man had children, all his sons would be normal, and not transmit the condition; but all his daughters would be carriers. This can be seen from Figure 12.

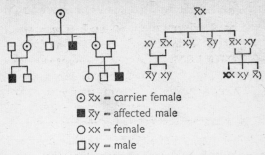

⊙ x̄x = carrier female

■ x̄y = affected male

○ xx = female

□ xy = male

11. The inheritance of haemophilia

|  | *Mother's germ cells* | |
|---|---|---|
| | $(\frac{1}{2})$X | $(\frac{1}{2})$X |
| $(\frac{1}{2})\bar{X}$ | $(\frac{1}{4})\bar{X}$X<br>carrier girl | $(\frac{1}{4})\bar{X}$X<br>carrier girl |
| $(\frac{1}{2})$Y | $(\frac{1}{4})$XY<br>normal boy | $(\frac{1}{4})$XY<br>normal boy |

*Father's germ cells*

12. The children of a haemophiliac man

The upper squares are carrier girls and the two lower squares normal boys. When the haemophiliac man's daughters come to have children, half their sons will be affected and half their daughters carriers, as can be seen in Figure 13.

|  | *Mother's germ cells* | |
|---|---|---|
| | $(\frac{1}{2})\bar{X}$ | $(\frac{1}{2})$X |
| $(\frac{1}{2})$X | $(\frac{1}{4})\bar{X}$X<br>carrier girl | $(\frac{1}{4})$XX<br>normal girl |
| $(\frac{1}{2})$Y | $(\frac{1}{4})\bar{X}$Y<br>haemo-<br>philiac boy | $(\frac{1}{4})$XY<br>normal boy |

*Father's germ cells*

13. The children of a carrier woman
(haemophilia)

The family tree of the descendants of an affected man are therefore likely to be as in Figure 14.

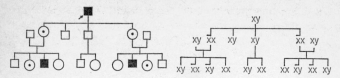

14. The descendants of a haemophilic man

It is not impossible for a girl to have haemophilia, and two examples have been described recently in this country; but to have the disease the girl must be homozygous for the recessive gene. Such a genotype can be produced if an affected man is unlucky enough to marry a woman who is a carrier. The possible children, then, are affected girls, carrier girls, affected boys, and normal boys, each with a probability of one in four, as may be seen from Figure 15.

|  | *Mother's germ cells* | |
|---|---|---|
|  | $(\frac{1}{2})\overline{X}$ | $(\frac{1}{2})X$ |
| $(\frac{1}{2})\overline{X}$ | $(\frac{1}{4})\overline{XX}$ <br> haemo- <br> philic girl | $(\frac{1}{4})\overline{X}X$ <br> carrier girl |
| $(\frac{1}{2})Y$ | $(\frac{1}{4})\overline{X}Y$ <br> haemo- <br> philic boy | $(\frac{1}{4})XY$ <br> normal boy |

*Father's germ cells*

15. The children of a haemophilic man and a carrier woman (haemophilia)

If a haemophilic woman marries and has children one would expect all her sons to be affected and all her daughters to be carriers, since all a haemophilic woman's egg cells will contain an $X$ chromosome with the gene for haemophilia.

Queen Victoria was a carrier of haemophilia, and her

carrier daughters introduced the gene into the Russian and the Spanish royal families. Her son King Edward VII did not inherit the gene so could not transmit it to his descendants.

## Linkage with the Y chromosome

In man the $Y$ chromosome is short and so one would not expect it to carry many gene-loci. In theory an unusual character determined by a gene on the part of the $Y$ chromosome which is unmatched by the $X$ chromosome would give a very characteristic family tree. Once the character has appeared, all the subsequent male descendants would be affected in the same way, since a man always transmits his $Y$ chromosome to his son and with it the gene for the character. A much-quoted example was that of the 'Porcupine Men'. These were men with a striking thickening and blackening of the skin. The first affected man was born in Suffolk in 1716. The story was that all his six sons were affected and that all the direct male line of descent for four further generations, but no women or girls, were similarly affected. Recently Stern from America and Penrose in England have re-examined the evidence after an exhaustive search of the parish registers. They found that there were almost certainly unaffected males in the pedigree and possibly affected females. Probably, in this family, as in others in which the same condition has occurred, the abnormality was due to a dominant gene. Further details of this family and the correct pedigree are shown in Chapter 8. There are probably no certain cases of $Y$-linked inheritance yet known, though some will almost certainly be found.

## Sex-limitation

A situation which is often confused with *X-chromosomal* sex-linkage is sex-limitation. In sex-limitation the condition is also, for practical purposes, confined to males, but the reason is not sex-linkage but that the genotype only manifests itself in males.

An example of this is a common form of premature baldness, which runs in certain families. This is due to a dominant gene which has an effect only on men. Women can inherit it from their fathers and transmit to their sons, but do not show it themselves. The distinction from sex-linkage, where the gene concerned is on the X chromosome, is readily made by the fact that in sex-limitation, but not sex-linkage, men can transmit the condition to their sons. The family patterns one finds are as in Figure 16.

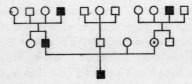

16. Family patterns in sex-limited inheritance

### The early recognition of sex

The sex of a child can be recognized as early as the eleventh week of foetal life by microscopic examination of cells withdrawn from the amniotic fluid surrounding the foetus. The withdrawal of fluid involves some risk and so should not be done without good reason.

Sooner or later it is probable that parents will be able to choose the sex of each of their children. The sperm carrying the X chromosome must be different in several ways from that carrying the Y chromosome.

# CHAPTER 4

# Blood Groups and Plasma Proteins

THE genetic basis for most normal human variation is not likely to be simple. A child's growth will depend for most characteristics on the satisfactory functioning of many chemical processes, each under independent genetic control. It will not be easy to recognize the influence of individual genes without sensitive chemical tests. Blood is an exceptional tissue in that it is easy to collect specimens repeatedly for chemical analysis, and at present the blood system is the only one for which we can detect the action of many single genes through the substances they directly produce. With other characters the normal variation we notice is usually the massed secondary effects of many genes and this is discussed in Chapter 6. However, recent developments in tissue culture, whereby a very small specimen of tissue can be freely grown in the laboratory, will make it much easier to analyse other tissues such as liver, bone, or muscle in the future. A fairly full account of blood group genetics is given in this chapter because they illustrate the amount of detail we may hope to have in time for other systems.

Blood is composed of two main parts: cells and liquid. The cells are red (see Plate 1a) or white (see Plate 1b, left of centre), the red containing the oxygen-carrying pigment, haemoglobin. The liquid part, known as plasma, contains a great variety of chemicals in solution and is the means by which salts, food, hormones, and the proteins conferring immunity to infection are transported from one organ to another (see Figure 17). Our most detailed knowledge is of the inheritance of the chemical substances in the envelope of the red blood cells which determine the 'blood group'.

Something is known about the inheritance of variations in the haemoglobin inside the red cells, but the variations are not, perhaps, normal and will be discussed later. Something too, is known about the heredity of normal variations of the proteins in the plasma.

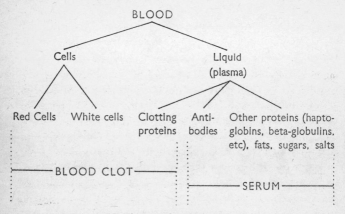

17. The constituents of blood

*Blood transfusion*

The blood-group substances which are of greatest practical importance in medicine are those determining the ABO types and the Rhesus types. One of the medical services of which Britain is justly proud is the National Blood Transfusion Service. Large numbers of adults regularly and voluntarily give a pint of their blood to the service, and this blood is then supplied to hospitals as the need arises. Blood transfusion is not only important in the treatment of casualties, but it has made possible a whole series of new operations, for example operations on the heart itself.

When a blood donor goes for the first time to give a donation, a few drops of blood are taken from his finger, and his ABO group is determined. Later his Rhesus group is also determined. The medical services then know for which patients the donor's blood may safely be used, though it is also the practice, whenever time permits, to have a direct check of some of the red cells from the donated blood against the serum of the patient.

## ABO system

Three of the ABO groups were first described from Austria by Landsteiner in 1900 and the fourth was discovered in 1902. The groups are A, B, AB, and O and the chemical substances in the envelopes of the red cells which determine the groups are called A, B, AB, and O substances. These substances belong to the group of chemicals known as glycoproteins and are made up of sugars and aminoacids. The importance of the A, B, and AB substances for blood transfusion is that men and women who do *not* possess a particular one of these substances in their own red cells have an antibody in the liquid part of their blood, the plasma, which will combine with that substance in foreign red cells introduced by transfusion. This causes the cells to clump and be destroyed. It was this reaction which made transfusion too unreliable to be used in medical practice before 1900. Sometimes it worked, but only too often the donor's red cells were clumped and destroyed by antibodies in the patient's plasma. This not only made the transfusion useless, but sometimes led to the death of the patient.

In practice, in testing for the substances in red cells it is usual to use serum rather than plasma. Serum is the liquid left after blood has clotted. It differs from plasma in that not only are the cells removed in the clot, but also those of the plasma proteins which are involved in clot formation. The blood group antibodies, however, are left in the serum, and a serum containing such antibodies is known as an antiserum.

In testing the ABO group of a donor, a drop of his blood is first tested with a strong anti-A serum. If the donor's cells are clumped by this serum, this is called a 'positive reaction' (shown as + in Figure 18) and means that the donor belongs to group A or group AB. Then another drop of his blood is tested with a strong anti-B serum and, if this serum clumps the cells, it means that the donor belongs to group B or AB. Accordingly, if neither serum clumps his cells, then the donor belongs to group O; if both sera clump his cells he belongs to group AB; if only anti-A clumps his cells he belongs to group A; if only anti-B clumps his cells he belongs to group B. This is illustrated in the chequer-board Figure 18.

*Reaction of cells with anti-*A

|  | − | + |
|---|---|---|
| − | O | A |
| + | B | AB |

*Reaction of cells with anti-*B

18. Reaction of cells with anti-A and anti-B sera

Group A individuals have an A substance on their cells, group B individuals a B substance. Group AB individuals have a substance which is probably more than a mixture of A and B substance, but gives the reaction of such a mixture. Group O individuals have neither A nor B substance. In their serum O individuals have anti-A and anti-B, A individuals anti-B, B individuals anti-A, and AB individuals neither anti-A nor anti-B.

AB patients can receive blood from the individuals of any group, but O patients can only receive blood from those who are also group O; A patients can receive group O or A blood; B patients can receive O or B blood.

Studies of the inheritance of the ABO groups have clear-cut results, which again can be summarized in chequer-board form in Figure 19. The children's groups are shown in the squares.

*Mother's group*

|  | O | A | B | AB |
|---|---|---|---|---|
| O | O | O or A | O or B | A or B |
| A | O or A | O or A | O or A or B or AB | A or B or AB |
| B | O or B | O or A or B or AB | O or B | A or B or AB |
| AB | A or B | A or B or AB | A or B or AB | A or B or AB |

*Father's group* (row labels)

19. The inheritance of the ABO blood groups

Thus a father and mother who are both group O are found only to have O children, and group B children are only found in families where father or mother is group B or AB. One of the early theories to explain these findings was that there were two pairs of genes concerned. A gene called *A* responsible for the production of substance A and an allele (alternative gene) producing no substance which one might call *a*, and a second separate pair at another gene locus with *B*, the gene producing substance B, and an allele producing no substance which one might call *b*. This system would give A, B, AB, and O individuals, the O individuals being those who have the genotype *aabb* and in whom no antigen is produced, A individuals being *AAbb* or *Aabb*, and B individuals being *aaBB* or *aaBb*. It would explain some of the genetic findings, for example that an A × B mating could produce A, B, or O children, provided that both the A and B individuals concerned also carried the alleles *a* and *b*. This is shown in Figure 20, with the children's groups and genetic constitutions in the squares. But this hypothesis does not explain, for example, the finding that an AB × O mating produces only A and B, and no O children.

A(*Aabb*) *parent's germ cells*

|  | *ab* | *Ab* |
|---|---|---|
| *ab* | O (*aabb*) | A (*Aabb*) |
| *aB* | B (*aaBb*) | AB (*AaBb*) |

B(*aaBb*) *parent's germ cells*

20. Children of an A(*Aabb*) parent and a B(*aaBb*) parent on the two locus theory

A better hypothesis to explain the genetic findings was put forward independently by Bernstein of Germany and Furuhata of Japan in 1927. They suggested that only one pair of genes was concerned in each individual and that there were three alleles which this individual might possess; gene *A* producing substance A, gene *B* producing substance B, and gene *O* producing nothing. This hypothesis is satisfactory except that the third gene is probably producing an O substance, since one team has found a serum which will agglutinate red cells from group-O individuals. On this theory an O individual will be genetically *OO*, and an A individual genetically *AA* or *AO*, a B individual genetically *BB* or *BO*, and an AB individual genetically *AB*. This explains all the genetic findings.

For example, the children of two AB individuals can be *AA*, that is A, *BB*, that is B, and *AB*, AB, as shown in Figure 21.

AB *parent's germ cells*

| | *A* | *B* |
|---|---|---|
| *A* | *AA* | *AB* |
| *B* | *AB* | *BB* |

(left axis label: AB *parent's germ cells*)

21. The children of two AB parents
on the single locus theory

One would not expect any of the children to be O.

Geneticists have suggested, to the research workers in the blood groups, that the genes should have symbols such as $I^a$, $I^b$, and $I^o$, but this has not yet been adopted.

In 1911 a rare subgroup of A was discovered which was in some ways intermediate between the commoner form of A and O. So A is now subdivided into $A_1$ and $A_2$, the latter being nearer to O. Genetically, $A_2$ behaves as if it were produced by an allele of $A_1$, *B*, and *O*. Very rare varieties, $A_3$ and $A_4$, have also been found, Similarly, there are rare groups known as $O_h$ and $B_w$. The true situation is, therefore, that there are probably many allelomorphs, but the common ones are the genes producing $A_1$ and $A_2$, B, and O substances.

While the red blood cells are the bodily system for which the ABO groups were discovered and for which they are of practical importance, other body fluids may also be imprinted in the same way. In 1930 it was discovered that people could be divided into 'secretors' and 'non-secretors' according to whether their saliva also contained substances with the same A, B, AB, or O specificity as their bloods. The distinction between secretor and non-secretor is difficult to make in some individuals; but in general secretion behaves as if due to a dominant gene. That is to say that the children of two non-secretors are always non-secretors, but that a proportion of the children of two secretors may be non-secretors. The symbol *Se* is used for the gene for secretion, and *se* for non-secretion. Non-secretors will be genetically *sese* and secretors may be *Sese* or *SeSe*. In secretors most tissues show A, B, or O specificity. Large amounts of group-specific substance are found, for example, in cysts of the ovary, in the first stools of a baby, and in seminal fluid. They are also found in the cells of the skin and this has recently been used to determine the ABO group of a human foetus from the shed skin cells floating in the amniotic fluid as early as the twelfth week of foetal life. It has also been found possible to detect the ABO groups of muscle tissue from mummies some 4,000 years old.

## The MNSs system

The second blood-group system was not discovered till twenty-seven years later, in 1927. This is the *MN* system to which is now added the S and s system, since it is known that the genes for s and s are either part of the genes for the M and N groups or are very closely linked to them. The discovery was more difficult than that for the ABO groups, since sera do not normally react with the M and N substances in the red cells. Antibodies to N substance will only develop in the blood of an M individual if he is transfused with N blood and *vice versa*. To make this discovery Landsteiner and Levine first prepared antibodies to human blood by injecting human blood into rabbits and then tested the sera with various samples of red blood cells. In this way they were able to prepare two sera. Some bloods are agglutinated by one of these and are said to be M, some by the other and are said to be N, and some are agglutinated by both sera and are called MN. These groupings were quite independent of the ABO groups, that is to say M, N, and MN individuals are found equally among A, B, AB, and O individuals.

Landsteiner and Levine suggested that two alleles determined these groups, one determining M and one determining N. On this theory an M individual would be genetically *MM*, an N individual genetically *NN*, and an MN individual genetically *MN*. The results of family studies on which this hypothesis was based were that M and M marriages gave all M children; N and N marriages gave all N children; while MN and M marriages on the average gave half M and half MN children; similarly MN × N marriages gave half N and half MN children and finally MN and MN marriages gave a quarter M, a quarter N, and half MN children. The last three results can be quickly checked in figure 22.

| | AN MN × M MARRIAGE | | AN MN × N MARRIAGE | | AN MN × MN MARRIAGE | |
|---|---|---|---|---|---|---|
| | M *parent's germ cells* | | N *parent's germ cells* | | MN *parent's germ cells* | |
| | | M | | N | $(\frac{1}{2})$M | $(\frac{1}{2})$N |
| MN *parent's germ cells* | $(\frac{1}{2})$M | $(\frac{1}{2})$MM | $(\frac{1}{2})$M | $(\frac{1}{2})$MN | $(\frac{1}{4})$MM | $(\frac{1}{4})$MN |
| | $(\frac{1}{2})$N | $(\frac{1}{2})$MN | $(\frac{1}{2})$N | $(\frac{1}{2})$NN | $(\frac{1}{4})$MN | $(\frac{1}{4})$NN |

22. The inheritance of the *MN* blood groups

As with the ABO groups, rare sub-varieties of the M and N antigens occur. A weak form of N, called $N_2$, has been reported several times, behaving as a third alternative gene at the *MN* locus. Unusual forms of M have also been reported of which one is intermediate between N and M. These are attributed to further alleles of the gene responsible for the M and N antigens.

Blood group s was discovered in 1947 from a sample of serum sent to England from Australia which contained anti-s. It was rapidly found that group s was associated with the *MN* system, but not with any other known system. The existence of an alternative gene to *S*, called s, was confirmed with the discovery of an anti-s serum in America in 1951. With the two anti-sera it became possible to divide people into group s (genetically *SS*), group ss (genetically *Ss*), and group s (genetically *ss*). Parents both *SS* were found to have, as might be expected, all *SS* children. Similarly, parents both *ss* had all *ss* children. Parents both *Ss* had *SS*, *Ss*, and *ss* children in the proportions of $\frac{1}{4}$, $\frac{1}{2}$, $\frac{1}{4}$.

The relationship of the *M* and *N* gene-locus to that for *S* and *s* was found to be very close, so close that it is uncertain whether there are two gene-loci close together on the same chromosome or whether complex alleles at a single gene-locus are concerned in producing both the MN and ss substances. In family studies any particular combination of *M* or *N* with *S* or *s* is inherited as a unit; there is no crossing-over. There are four such combinations possible on a single chromosome, *MS*, *Ms*, *NS*, and *Ns*.

## The $P_1P_2\,p$ system

The third system to be discovered was that of the P types. This was also found in 1927 by Landsteiner and Levine, who prepared anti-P by immunizing rabbits with human red cells. About three-quarters of European bloods react to anti-P and about one-quarter do not. Reaction to anti-P, implying the possession of the P substance, behaves in families as if due to a dominant gene. Soon after its discovery anti-P was found to occur naturally and now it seems probable that, just as for the ABO groups men and women without A possess anti-A and without B possess anti-B, so non-P individuals possess anti-P. But this naturally-occurring anti-P is weak.

Since 1955 three alleles have been recognized for this

system, $P_1$, $P_2$, and $p$, with two naturally occurring anti-sera. One of these anti-sera found in the rare $pp$ individuals clumps the cells of those containing $P_1$ or $P_2$ substance; the other is a rather weak anti-serum found in those who are $P_2P_2$ or $pP_2$, which clumps cells containing $P_1$ substance.

## The Rhesus system

The fourth group of blood types, the Rhesus series, is as important in medicine as the ABO group. While the ABO group is important for transfusion, the Rhesus group has been shown to be responsible for the illness or death, shortly before or after birth, from destruction of the red blood cells, of about one child in 200 in the white races. As long ago as 1905 evidence was produced showing that a mother might be immunized by the A or B antigens of the baby she was carrying. The possibility will arise whenever a father has a gene for a blood-group antigen which the mother does not possess. For example, an OO mother married to an AO father will have AO and OO children. The red cells of the AO children would be agglutinated if they got into the mother's serum and they would reinforce the strength of her natural anti-A antibodies. In 1945 it was shown that this did in fact occur provided that the child was a secretor.

In 1938 the American physician, Darrow, suggested that the not uncommon disease of infancy where the baby's red cells are rapidly destroyed might be due to antibodies from the mother. The baby's red cells were destroyed because they stimulated the formation of antibodies in the mother's circulation, and these antibodies passed back into the baby's circulation. The following year Levine and Stetson reported that a mother who had had a still-born child was transfused with some of her husband's blood; and the red cells of this donated blood were rapidly destroyed. It was found that this mother's serum contained an antibody which clumped the red cells of roughly 80 per cent of O individuals. Levine and Stetson suggested that the child and father had an antigen not present in the mother, and the child had sensitized the mother to this antigen.

The next step was the discovery in 1940 by Landsteiner and Wiener that if a rabbit was immunized with the blood of the Macacus rhesus monkey an antibody was produced which agglutinated the red cells of 84 per cent of the white population of New York. Those whose red cells were agglutinated were called Rhesus positive and the 16 per cent whose red cells were not agglutinated Rhesus negative. Shortly after, Wiener and Peters found this antibody in some of the individuals who had a reaction after transfusion of the correct ABO group, including Levine and Stetson's patient. Finally, in 1941, Levine and his colleagues showed that most of the cases of destruction of the red cells in the new-born were due to sensitization of a Rh negative mother by a Rh positive child.

Fortunately, most Rh negative women married to Rh positive husbands never develop antibodies and have healthy babies. About 13 per cent of marriages in Britain are between a Rh negative woman and a Rh positive man. But only about one child in 200 has its red cells destroyed by anti-Rh antibodies. Once, however, a Rh negative woman has developed antibodies then any further Rh positive child she has will be affected. Fortunately, if the baby is born alive there is an effective treatment. This is to give the baby a large transfusion of Rh negative blood, replacing much of the baby's own damaged red cells by the transfused cells. The reasons why some women do not develop antibodies are not fully known. But one known mechanism is that, where the child's ABO group is also incompatible with the mother's, for example an A baby of an O mother, the mother does not develop Rh antibodies. The probable reason is that any of the baby's red cells escaping into the mother's circulation are destroyed on account of the ABO incompatibility before they can cause Rhesus sensitization.

Further investigation showed that the antigens of the Rhesus group and the genes responsible for them were complicated. A brilliant hypothesis was put forward by Fisher, in 1944. He suggested that there were three closely linked gene-loci concerned. At each gene-locus there were two main possible alternative genes named $C$ and $c$, $D$ and $d$, $E$ and $e$, each producing a substance. There would then be eight alternative Rhesus gene combinations on a chromosome, and these are shown in Figure 23, together with the alternative symbols (American). On the two members of the pair of chromosomes concerned a man or woman could have any of the thirty-six different combinations of these eight.

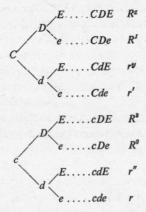

| | | |
|---|---|---|
| $E$ . . . . $CDE$ | $R^z$ |
| $e$ . . . . . $CDe$ | $R^1$ |
| $E$ . . . . . $CdE$ | $r^y$ |
| $e$ . . . . . $Cde$ | $r'$ |
| $E$ . . . . . $cDE$ | $R^2$ |
| $e$ . . . . . $cDe$ | $R^0$ |
| $E$ . . . . . $cdE$ | $r''$ |
| $e$ . . . . . $cde$ | $r$ |

23. Alternative Rhesus chromosomes

Since anti-D is responsible for most cases of Rhesus incompatibility between a mother and her child, those individuals with $D$ on at least one chromosome are said to be Rh positive and the remainder are called Rh negative.

Anti-sera to each of the postulated antigens have been

T – C

found; anti-D is the one most often found and, as was said above, is the anti-serum responsible for the great majority of cases of red-cell destruction in the new-born. Anti-C and anti-E are also not uncommon. In contrast, anti-d has only been reported twice, and there is no confirmation of either of these claims. Because of this, while a man or woman whose red cells do not react to anti-D serum may reasonably be supposed to have the genotype *dd*, an individual who does react may have the genotype *DD* or *Dd*. It is often a matter of considerable practical importance to decide which a man has. If a couple have had a child with red-cell destruction, mother being *dd* and sensitized to D, then the outlook for further pregnancies depends on the husband's genotype. If he is *DD* then any children will be *Dd*, receiving *D* from the father and *d* from mother, and will very probably suffer from the disease, since once a mother has been sensitized then any subsequent *D* children are likely to be affected. On the other hand, if the husband is *Dd*, then there is an even chance that any subsequent child will be *dd*, the same as the mother, and not affected by the mother's anti-D. Fortunately the other antigens present will often indicate whether *DD* or *Dd* is the more likely genotype of the father. This is because certain combinations of antigens are commoner than others. For example, a man whose blood reacts to anti-C, anti-D, and anti-e, but not to anti-c and anti-E, will have *CDe* on one chromosome, but might have *CDe* or *Cde* on the other. Since *CDe* is some forty-one times as common in the population of England as *Cde*, the former is more likely. Recent work by Clarke and his colleagues in Liverpool proves that antibody production in *dd* mothers may be prevented by giving them anti-D serum soon after the birth, whenever it can be shown that *Dd* red cells from the baby have entered the mother's circulation.

Remembering that, for practical purposes, there is no crossing-over, the inheritance of the genes for the Rhesus blood types is straightforward. For example, taking parents of the most common and the next most common genotypes, *CDe/cde* and *CDe/CDe*, children will have an even chance of being *CDe/CDe* or *CDe/cde*. The third commonest genotype is *cde/cde* and a mating of a parent of this genotype with one of genotype *CDe/cde* would give children with an even chance of being *CDe/cde* or *cde/cde*.

As with other gene-loci controlling other blood groups, further alleles are being discovered. These include $C^w$, $D^u$, and $E^u$.

### The concept of gene frequency

In addition to the frequency of particular blood-group genotypes in the population, it is possible to calculate the frequencies of the individual alleles, the gene frequency. This is the proportion of individual chromosomes, for example in germ cells, that contain the alleles. The concept of gene frequency is a useful one, particularly when comparing different populations. The way in which the gene frequency is estimated is shown below.

[The reader who does not like arithmetic may prefer to skip the rest of this section.]

If there are two alleles at a gene-locus, it is usual to call the frequency of one $p$ and the other $q$, $p$ and $q$ being fractions which add up to one. Thus, if two genes are equally common, half the chromosomes in the population carrying one and half the other, $p = \frac{1}{2}$ and $q = \frac{1}{2}$; if one gene is three times as common as another, then $p$, the frequency of the first, is $\frac{3}{4}$, and $q$, the frequency of the second, is $\frac{1}{4}$. In 1908 an English mathematician, Hardy, and a German, Weinberg, noted independently that, if there were no tendency for people of the same genotype to marry each other preferentially, gene frequencies of $p$ and $q$ for, say genes $X$ and $x$ would give genotype frequencies of $p^2$ for $XX$, $2pq$ for $Xx$, and $q^2$ for $xx$. This is readily seen from Figure 24 in which the genotypes and their frequencies are entered in the squares.

*One chromosome*

|  | gene X $(p)$ | gene x $(q)$ | total |
|---|---|---|---|
| gene X $(p)$ | XX $(p^2)$ | Xx $(pq)$ | $(p^2 + pq)$ |
| gene x $(q)$ | Xx $(pq)$ | xx $(q^2)$ | $(pq + q^2)$ |
| total | $(p^2 + pq)$ | $(pq + q^2)$ | 1 |

*Other chromosome*

24. Genotype frequencies derived from the gene frequencies in a population

It will be noted that since $p + q = 1$, $p^2 + 2pq + q^2 = (p + q)^2 = 1$.

This formula may be used to calculate the genotype frequencies, on the assumption of random mating, from the gene frequencies. For example, if $p$ and $q$ are both $\frac{1}{2}$, then the frequencies of the two homozygotes XX and xx are each $\frac{1}{4}$, and the frequency of the heterozygotes Xx is $\frac{1}{2}$. The formula is more often used to calculate the gene frequencies from the genotype frequencies. For example, out of 1,279 English people the genotype frequencies for the MN types were MM 0·284, MN 0·496, NN 0·220. From these the gene frequencies can be counted, that of M being the frequency of MM, plus half that for MN, that is $0·284 + \frac{1}{2}(0·496) = 0·532$. Similarly, the gene frequency of N is $0·220 + \frac{1}{2}(0·496) = 0·468$. There are in fact slightly fewer MN individuals in this sample than would be expected from the frequencies of MM and NN, since from the gene frequencies calculated, the MN individuals should be 1,279 × 2pq, that is 1,279 × 2 ×

$0 \cdot 532 \times 0 \cdot 468 = 636 \cdot 9$ and not the observed 634. But this is the kind of difference that might well have arisen by chance. An alternative method of arriving at the gene frequency of $M$ and $N$ would be to take the square root of the frequency of MM and NN respectively. This would give nearly the same results, but is less efficient as it does not make use of the information provided by the number of MN individuals.

When the closely linked substance s was tested at the same time as the MN antigens, the distribution of phenotypes of 1,419 English people was found to be:

MMS 295 (0·208),    MNS 379 (0.267),    NNS 102 (0·072),
MsMs 107 (0 075),    MsNs 322 (0·227),    NsNs 214 (0·151).

The most efficient method for calculating the gene frequencies from this phenotypic distribution is complex, as in all cases where the exact genotype cannot be determined. It was devised for the Rhesus system by Fisher and gives frequencies of:

$MS \ 0 \cdot 247, \ Ms \ 0 \cdot 283, \ NS \ 0 \cdot 080, \ Ns \ 0 \cdot 390,$

from which in turn the expected proportion of different genotypes may be calculated; for example, $MSMS$ will be $(0 \cdot 247)^2$ or 0.061, and $MSMs$ will be $2 \times 0 \cdot 247 \times 0 \cdot 283$ or $0 \cdot 140$. These two combine to give the expected phenotype frequency of $MMS$ (since in the absence of anti-s they cannot be distinguished serologically) of $0 \cdot 201$, which does not differ significantly from the observed frequency of 0.208.

Similarly with the ABO blood groups: since, for example, the genotype $A_1 A_2$ cannot be distinguished (except by family studies in some cases) from $A_1 O$, the frequencies for the genes $A$, $B$, and $O$ cannot be determined by counting but must be calculated. For southern England they are: $O$ $0 \cdot 616$, $A_1$ $0 \cdot 259$, $A_2$ $0 \cdot 065$, $B$ $0 \cdot 060$. Northern England and, even more, Scottish, North Welsh, and Irish surveys show higher frequencies of o and lower of a.

The gene frequencies for the P group are not reliably worked out, but in Europe it appears that $p$ is rare and $P_1$ and $P_2$ each have a frequency of about 0·5.

For the Rhesus types, as with $MNSs$, the individual gene frequencies are not of much interest, except in the case of $D$ and $d$ because of their importance for red-cell destruction of the new-born. These are $D$ 0·590 and $d$ 0·410, giving roughly 17 per cent Rhesus negative $dd$ individuals and 83 per cent Rh positive $Dd$ and $DD$. It is the closely linked groups of genes that are of interest and in England three are common:

$CDe$ 0·407, $cde$ 0·389, $cDE$ 0·141

five are reasonably common:

$cDe$ 0·026, $C^wDe$ and $cdE$ 0·012, $Cde$ 0·010, $CDE$ 0·002

and the remainder are rare.

*Other blood-group systems*

Since 1945 a number of further substances on the red cells have been found. In each case the discovery came from the finding of an unusual anti-serum in a man or woman who had been transfused or a woman who had been sensitized by a pregnancy. The names of the systems, the symbols for the chemical substances, the years of their discovery, and the approximate frequencies of the genes in the English population are shown in Table 2.

Table 2. Gene frequencies for the
blood-group systems discovered
since 1945

| | | | | | | |
|---|---|---|---|---|---|---|
| Lutheran | $Lu^a$ | 1946 | 0·04 | $Lu^b$ | 1956 | 0·96 |
| Kell | K | 1946 | 0·05 | k | 1950 | 0·95 |
| Lewis | $Le^a$ | 1946 | 0·47 | $Le^b$ | 1948 | 0·52 |
| Duffy | $Fy^a$ | 1950 | 0·59 | $Fy^b$ | 1951 | 0·41 |
| Kidd | $Jk^a$ | 1951 | 0·51 | $Jk^b$ | 1953 | 0·49 |

All these blood types are inherited independently of each other, with the exception of the Lutheran gene-locus which is closely linked with the Lewis or with the secretor gene-locus, which determines whether ABO specific substances are secreted into the saliva.

## A sex-linked blood group

An important further blood-group system was discovered early in 1962. An American in Grand Rapids, U.S.A., who had had repeated transfusions because he suffered from a bleeding disorder, was found to have in his blood an anti-serum which reacted with the red-blood cells of 62 per cent of American men and 89 per cent of American women. The gene producing the antigen was called $Xg^a$, and its so far silent allele $Xg$. Family studies carried out with the help of the Lister Institute in London soon showed that the gene locus concerned must be on the $X$ chromosome. For example, men who reacted with the anti-serum, said to be xg (a+), married to women who did not react, said to be xg (a−), had sons who were all xg (a−) like their mothers and daughters who were all xg (a+) like their fathers. These daughters would have the genotype $Xg^aXg$. The gene frequency of $Xg^a$ is directly given by the proportion of men who give positive reactions and so is about 0·62.

For a time supplies of this valuable anti-serum depended on the single donor. But, other sources have been found, and studies of cross-over values between this gene locus and those of other sex-linked genes will greatly help the mapping of the gene loci on the $X$ chromosome. Unfortunately, however, work hitherto suggests that the $Xg$ locus is at one end of the $X$ chromosome and not very close to any of the already known sex-linked loci.

## Uniqueness of an individual's blood group

The genes for the blood-group antigens, even by themselves,

illustrate a point to be deduced from the mechanism of inheritance, that each individual, identical twins excepted, is unique. Use is made of this, for example, in identification in police work. Using the blood-group systems mentioned earlier there are 303,264 different phenotypic combinations possible in Englishmen. A sample of blood from a man or woman would often not be matched in a group of 100 other individuals. The director of the Medical Research Council's Blood Group Research Unit in London estimates that even the *commonest* combination in England, O, MSNs, $P_1$, CDe/cde, $Lu^bLu^b$, kk, $Le^bLe^b$, $Fy^aFy^b$, $Jk^aJk^b$, occurs only once in about 270 people. It is almost as unwise for a murderer to leave a specimen of his blood at the site of the crime as to leave a finger-print. Similarly, as mentioned in Chapter 1, blood groups are the best way of testing whether twins are identical or fraternal. If the twins differ on any group, then, unless one has been recently transfused, they are fraternal. But if they are found to be the same for each group, where from the parents' groups they might have differed, the case against their being fraternal is built up, usually to a probability of about thirty-two to one. For example, if one twin is group O and father and mother are both A, then the probability of the second twin, if fraternal, also being group O is only a quarter. If one twin is N and the parents are both MN then the probability that the other twin will also be N, if fraternal, is again a quarter, and the combined odds on these two groups alone against the twins being fraternal is fifteen to one.

*Blood groups in paternity suits*

Another obvious medico-legal use of the blood groups is in the cases of disputed paternity. In many countries, for example many American states and the Scandinavian countries, but not in Britain, when a mother of an illegitimate child brings a paternity suit against a man, the courts have the power to order blood-group tests on all three individuals. While it is never possible to prove that a man is the father of the child by blood groups, it is often possible to show that he could not be the father. The principle is that any blood-group substance which a child possesses and which his mother does not possess must have come from the father. If the alleged father does not possess this blood-group substance then he cannot be the father of the child, except in the exceedingly unlikely event of the gene concerned having changed its character between father and child.

About 60 per cent of men falsely alleged to be the father of an illegitimate child can, in theory, be exonerated in this way. Experience of blood-group tests in New York State and Sweden indicates that in these two areas nearly half the allegations of paternity are incorrect. When it is not possible definitely to exclude a particular man as the father it is possible to give an idea of how probable or improbable it is that he is the father, and in Sweden some weight is attached by the courts to these probabilities. For example, it is found in Sweden that in about 1 per cent of the cases, though the man being the father of the child cannot be excluded, the likelihood of his being the father is less than 3 per cent, and it needs strong evidence of other kinds before the paternity is assigned to him. In the same way where the choice lies between two men neither of whom can be excluded by blood groups, these may, nevertheless, indicate that one man is many times more likely to be the father than the other. Calculations of this kind may become especially important in the Scandinavian countries where legislation is proposed that will give an illegitimate child the same rights to inheritance of his father's property as legitimate children.

*Blood-group gene frequencies in anthropology: the picture in Europe*

Another and fascinating use of blood-group frequencies is in tracing connexions between different races. The discovery that races differed in the frequency in which the various blood groups are found was made by Professor and Mrs Hirszfeld in 1910. The distribution in Europe of the frequencies of the genes for the A, B, and O antigens have been compiled by Mourant and his colleagues and are shown in Figure 25. In the British Isles the blood groups, in spite of extensive internal migration, still show a contrast between the English- and Celtic-speaking peoples. In south-east England the frequency of the gene for A is between 25 and 30 per cent, in contrast to between 15 and 20 per cent in the Celtic-speaking areas. Conversely, the gene for O has a high frequency in the Celtic-speaking areas. The gene frequencies of $A$ in south-east England are similar to those of west and central Europe as a whole (including Scandinavia), which is an area relatively high in $A$.

The high $O$ and low $A$ frequency of the Celtic-speaking north and west fringes of the British Isles and also of Norse-speaking Iceland is paralleled in Europe only in the Basque-speaking parts of France and Spain and in Sardinia and Crete; but rather similar frequencies are found in the Berbers of North Africa and in the inhabitants of the western Caucasus in Asia. This agrees with the evidence from archaeology and physical anthropology. It would appear that Iron Age and Anglo-Saxon immigrants into south and east England partly displaced to the north and west earlier inhabitants who were descendants of New Stone Age immigrants from North Africa and the Iberian Peninsular, together with the remnants of even older peoples. As is often the case, although the Celtic-speaking Iron Age immigrants imposed their language on the people of the west and north of the British Isles, the biggest genetic contribution to the present-day population of these areas comes from the earlier peoples. Essentially the same early immigrants contributed most to the population of Iceland, though here it was the Norse-speaking Vikings, and not the Celts, who finally determined the national language.

As one goes across Europe the frequency of $B$ rises to over 10–15 per cent in eastern Germany, eastern Czechoslovakia, and Yugoslavia, with a further rise to 15–20 per cent in European Russia and eastern Finland and the Middle East, rising further to 20–25 per cent as one enters Asia. A pocket of high $B$ in north-east Sweden is due to immigration from Finland; another in south-west Spain is due to immigration from North Africa. The Magyar-speaking Hungarians do not differ from the surrounding Slav-speaking peoples. The highest $A$ frequencies are found in southern Norway, southern and central Finland, Portugal, and western Spain, regions of the Franco-German frontier, Switzerland, Romania, Bulgaria, and Turkey. The last five regions are all mountainous. Another high $A$ area is Lapland in the far north of Scandinavia, Finland, and Russia. This is, however, genetically quite distinct since the $A$ is predominantly $A_2$. $A_2$ occurs with a frequency of 5–10 per cent in the rest of Europe and in Africa, both north and south of the Sahara, but is rare elsewhere.

The general picture here is of a relatively and absolutely high $O$ people pushed into the corners of the European area, the extreme north-west, North Africa, the Mediterranean islands, and the Caucasus; of a solid central, relatively high $A$ people reaching up into Scandinavia and down into Spain, Italy, and Greece; and of an eastern relatively high $B$ people reaching, in attenuated form, as far as central Germany.

The Rhesus genes distinguish north and west Europe from the remainder of Europe, and indeed from the rest of the world so far studied except parts of North Africa, by the high frequency of the gene combination $cde$. This reaches its maximum in the Basque-speaking peoples on either side of the western boundary between France and Spain and

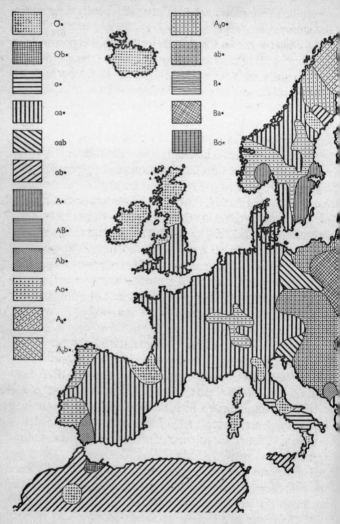

**25.** Distribution of blood-group genes *A*, *B*, and *O* in Europe (modified from Mourant, Kopec, and Sobczak)

Legend:

O•
Ob•
o•
oa•
oab
ob•
A•
AB•
Ab•
Ao•
A₀•
A₂b•

A₂o•
ab•
B•
Ba•
Bo•

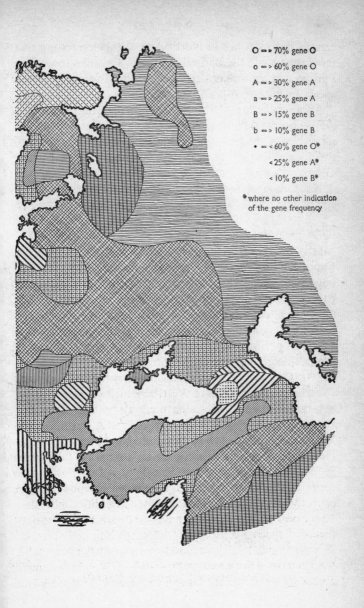

O ⟹ > 70% gene O
o ⟹ > 60% gene O
A ⟹ > 30% gene A
a ⟹ > 25% gene A
B ⟹ > 15% gene B
b ⟹ > 10% gene B
• ⟸ < 60% gene O*
     < 25% gene A*
     < 10% gene B*

* where no other indication
  of the gene frequency

certain Berber tribes in North Africa. It is interesting that the Basques and the Berbers are the two peoples in western Europe and the western part of North Africa who do not speak an Indo-European language.

Another feature of the British Isles is a high frequency (45–50 per cent) of the gene for N and a correspondingly low frequency of the gene for M. This is shared by Scandinavia, the Spanish Peninsula, and the very north-west of France, Germany, and Poland. In the rest of Europe the frequency of *N* is intermediate and then falls to low values as one enters Russia and central and southern Asia.

*Intercontinental differences in blood-group gene frequencies*

All the differences so far mentioned are within the white or Caucasian race. They are group differences, and it would be impossible reliably to assign any individual to a particular part of Europe on the basis of his blood groups alone. The differences between native European, native African, and native Mongolian are, as one might expect, much wider. A specimen of blood known to come from either a white or a West African Negro could be correctly labelled 95 times out of 100. The most effective distinction is by the Duffy groups; for example, 90 per cent of West Africans have no $Fy^a$ or $Fy^b$ substance, while all whites have one or both of these substances. Independently, 40 per cent of West Africans have the V substance (thought to be the product not of another gene-locus but of *c* and $e^s$ on the same chromosome) of the Rhesus groups and this is very rare in whites. Another substance genetically linked to the *MNSs* system, Hu, is found in 22 per cent of West Africans and not in whites. In addition more than 10 per cent of West Africans have one or other of the variant forms of the red-cell pigment haemoglobin, and these are very rare in whites. These blood-group substances are rather less effective in distinguishing between the blood of coloured and white citizens of the United States, and the blood-group gene frequencies indicate that the coloured population contains a considerable amount, 30 per cent or more, of white heredity. More blood substances will be found with a frequency sharply distinct in whites and Negroes; for example, a new substance was found in 1958, provisionally called Js, which is rare if not absent in whites, yet present in 20 per cent of American coloured people. All these specifically Negro characters would also be useful in distinguishing between native Africans and members of the Mongolian races, and have shown, for example, that there is no close connexion between Negroes and the superficially similar Melanesians. Fewer specific blood groups are known at the moment for the Mongolian races to distinguish them from the white races; they have been much less thoroughly investigated. The most effective distinction at any rate for some Mongolian races is by a blood-group substance, Diego (Di), which was first discovered in native South American Indians. It is present for example, in over 30 per cent of South American Carib Indians, and 10 per cent of Japanese, but is very rare in whites. In contrast the Rhesus gene complex *cde* is practically absent in Mongolians.

We cannot make full use of similarity in blood-group frequencies in tracing racial relationships until we know more of the natural selective forces to which they are subject and the rate at which they can change. It is already clear that blood groups provide a valuable check on conclusions drawn from physical anthropology, language, and history. Steps are now being taken to blood-group bones and it may be possible before long to determine the blood-group frequencies of populations living many centuries ago. There are already indications that the ABO frequencies do not normally change appreciably over periods of centuries. The descendants of German colonists who settled in Hungary two and a half centuries ago have a modern German distribution. The blood donors with English surnames in Northern Ireland have a modern English distribution, although they have been settled there for over four centuries. Nevertheless, the ABO groups are more variable geographically than the *MNSs* and Rhesus systems, indicating that the latter are even more stable.

Genetic differences of this kind are no reason for valuing one race of man more highly than another, nor do they necessarily indicate that inter-racial crossing is undesirable.

## Selective value of the blood groups

The state of affairs where several alleles each occur with a considerable frequency is called 'genetic polymorphism'. It is not easy to understand how this is maintained. Fisher showed that if one of these alternative genes conveys even a slight extra degree of 'fitness', in the sense that those who possess it are consistently likely to have more surviving children than those who do not, one would expect that gene to be common in the population and the others to be rare. Two explanations have been put forward for genetic polymorphism. The first is that the heterozygotes for these genes, those who are *AB*, *AO*, or *BO*, are fitter than the homozygotes *AA*, *BB*, and *OO*. Then even if *OO* individuals are fitter than *AA* individuals, the *A* gene will maintain itself in the population relative to *O* because *AO* individuals are fitter than either *AA* or *OO*. There is no evidence that this explanation is correct for the blood types in man, but many examples are known in such well-studied animals as the fruitfly, and one probable example is known in man in relation to sickle-cell haemoglobin, to which reference is made in Chapter 8. The other explanation that has been suggested is that in species of animals living in many different environments one form of the gene may have a selective advantage in one environment and another form in a different environment. Migration and intermarriage between the two populations would prevent the form of the gene, which was locally advantageous, from entirely ousting the other form from the population. There is no good evidence that this explanation is correct for the ABO groups, but indications that a process of this kind is possible comes from finding that individuals of some blood groups are more predisposed to certain diseases than others.

## Blood groups and disease

In 1953 the British surgeon, Aird, and his colleagues noted, for example, that cancer of the stomach was more prevalent in certain parts of the British Isles than others. Thinking that this difference might be of racial origin they collected information on the blood groups of these patients. To their surprise they found that in each area which they studied there were more group A individuals (who would be mostly genetically *AO*) and fewer group O individuals than in the general population of the same area. Similar findings have now been reported from North America and the continent of Europe. Persons of group A are about 20 per cent more prone to develop the disease than those of groups O or B.

Aird and his colleagues then turned their attention to the other common complaint of the stomach, ulcer of the stomach and the first part of the small intestine, the duodenum. They now found that it was those of group O who were unduly susceptible and this again has been confirmed in America and on the continent of Europe. More recent work has shown that this is true especially, perhaps only, for ulcers of the duodenum and the adjoining, rather than the main, part of the stomach. These differences in susceptibility are quite substantial and consistent in the different areas studied. A group O individual is about 40 per cent more likely to get duodenal ulcer than people of other groups. The selective pressure exerted by a duodenal ulcer would be much greater than that by cancer of the stomach. More recently it has been shown in Liverpool that there is an even stronger difference in the liability to duodenal ulcer between those who are secretors of blood-group specific substances and those who are not, the latter being 80 per cent more prone to ulcers than the secretors. There is now evidence that the *B* gene may protect against smallpox.

There is more direct selection of the genes for blood types where differences between mother and her unborn child may lead to death of the baby, as with the gene for the Rhesus D substance. Such a death will involve the loss of one of each allele, that is one *D* and one *d*, since the mother is homozygous *dd* and the father must have contributed a *D* gene. This will favour the survival of the more common gene which in Britain is the gene *D*. It has been suggested that the present frequency of the gene in western Europe is due to the mixture of two races, one high in *d* – best represented now in the Basques – and the other high in *D*. On this theory the gene for d is now being slowly eliminated except among the few groups where it is commoner than the gene for D. In the same way the occasional example of red cell destruction in the new-born due to a child being A and the mother O, favours the survival of the gene for O where *O* is the more common gene. As explained above, ABO incompatibility protects against Rhesus sensitization, so that the total balance of selective advantage and disadvantage of these genes from haemolytic disease of the new-born is complex.

*Plasma proteins*

The genetics of the liquid part of the blood, plasma, have only been intensively studied in the last few years. It is already clear, however, that there is much genetically determined normal variation in the types of the proteins in the plasma, though our knowledge is, as yet, much less detailed than for the substances in the envelopes of the red blood cells.

In 1955 the Canadian, Smithies, found that one of these kinds of protein, known as hapto-globin, existed in three forms which were called 1·1, 1·2, and 2·2. The proportions of North Americans and Englishmen with the form 1·1 is about 16 per cent, with the form 1·2 about 48 per cent, and with the form 2·2 about 36 per cent. Genetic studies showed that the differences are due to alleles at a single gene-locus, 1·1 being homozygous for one allele and 2·2 homozygous for the other allele, and 1·2 being heterozygotes with one of each allele.

One function of the hapto-globins is to hold on to the red-cell pigment, haemoglobin, when it is released into the plasma after destruction of the red cell and so prevent it being lost through the kidneys. This property is best effected by hapto-globin 1·1 and its high frequency in tropical Africa may be due to the need to prevent haemoglobin loss after destruction of red cells by malaria.

Another kind of protein in the plasma, the beta-globulins, has recently been found to exist in three genetically determined forms, B, C, and D. Most Canadians and Englishmen are homozygous for the allele producing C, but a few are heterozygous and have both B and C. On the other hand Negroes, both in Canada and Gambia, are mostly homozygous for the allele producing C, but a few have C and D. The form D is commonest among Australian aboriginals. One of the functions of the beta-globulins is to carry iron in the plasma.

# CHAPTER 5

# Further Single-Factor Inheritance for Normal Human Variation – 'Tasting', Colour-blindness, and Eye-colour

## Tasting phenylthiourea

ONCE we leave the blood, there are few characters in human beings which we know to be largely dependent on alternative genes at a single locus. One such character was discovered in 1931; this is the ability to taste a group of chemical compounds, of which phenylthiourea is typical.

To about 70 per cent of English and North Americans phenylthiourea has an unpleasant bitter taste; while the other 30 per cent do not taste the substance at all except in highly concentrated solution. The concentration of the chemical which best distinguishes between 'tasters', that is those who taste it readily, and 'non-tasters' varies with the age of the subjects. This is understandable, as one's general ability to taste lessens with increasing age. It is found that the best discrimination in adolescents is given by a solution of 40 milligrams of phenylthiourea in a litre of water. In people over the age of fifty the best discrimination is given by a solution four times as strong, that is 160 milligrams per litre.

Just as with the blood types, there are interesting racial differences in the proportion of 'tasters' and 'non-tasters' in a population. About 30 per cent of English people are 'non-tasters', but only about 5 per cent of Negroes and 10 per cent of Chinese.

The results of a study (by Harris and Kalmus of the Galton Laboratory in London) of the frequency distribution of the 'tasting' ability of 102 young (aged between sixteen and twenty-five) and 101 old (aged between sixy-six and eighty-five) Englishmen is shown in Figure 26. The horizontal axis in this diagram shows the minimum concentration that the men could taste. (Solution No. 1 was 1·3 gram of phenylthiourea per litre, No. 2 was half the strength, No. 3 a quarter of this strength, and so on.) The vertical axis shows the numbers of men who fell into each group. In both the young and the old men there are strong indications of two distinct types of individuals, those who could taste readily and those who could taste only strong concentrations or not at all, and the proportions of each type are about the same, approximately 30 per cent at each age; but the taste threshold of both types has shifted two or three classes towards the more concentrated solutions in the old men. However, in the old men particularly, the two types appear to overlap in their distributions.

Family studies show that the main difference between 'tasters' and 'non-tasters' is determined by a single gene-locus at which there are two alleles, one allele being dominant to the other and conferring the ability to taste. The evidence for this is that where both parents are 'non-tasters' all the children are 'non-tasters'. (The only exceptions are from parents in the zone of overlap of tasting ability of the two types.) Where both parents are 'tasters', or one is a 'taster' and one a 'non-taster', all the children are 'tasters' in some of the families, but in other families a proportion of the children are 'non-tasters'. Accordingly, if the gene conferring the ability to taste is called $Ta$, and the alternative $ta$, 'non-tasters' will be homozygous $tata$, but 'tasters' may be homozygous $TaTa$ or heterozygous $Tata$. The effect of these genotypes on the ability to taste is, however, modified by the person's age and probably by other factors both genetic and environmental. Among the Chinese, there is little or no overlap in the tasting ability of the two groups, so that practically all Chinese $tata$ individuals can be recognized by their weak powers of tasting phenylthiourea.

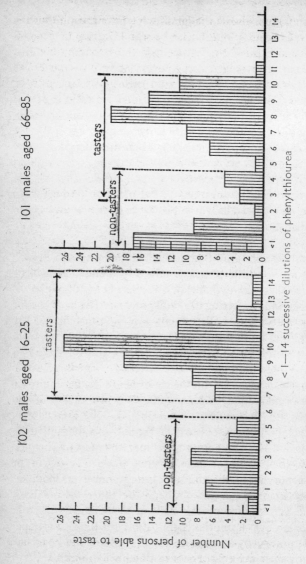

26. The distribution of 'tasting' ability in young and old men (after Harris and Kalmus)

The possible selective value of these differences in tasting ability is not known, but it may be related to the function of the thyroid gland. Some of the group of compounds distinguishing 'tasters' and 'non-tasters' have a markedly inhibitory effect on the ability of the thyroid gland to secrete its hormone. They are used for this reason as an alternative to an operation in treating patients whose thyroid gland is oversecreting. Recently an association has been found between tasting ability and certain diseases of the thyroid gland.

## Colour-blindness

Another nearly normal variation for which it is possible to recognize the effects of alleles at a single gene-locus is abnormality of colour vision. There are several different types. The most complete form is total colour-blindness. This form is rare and those affected see shades of light and dark but no colours at all. It behaves in families as if due to a recessive gene on one of the autosomes (i.e. on one of the chromosomes other than the $X$ chromosome.) The other types all involve colour-blindness for only one of the three main types of colour vision, that is the perception of red, blue, or green. There are six known types: three are severe and are called 'red-blindness', 'green-blindness',* and 'blue-blindness'; three are mild and are called 'red-weakness', green-weakness', and 'blue-weakness'. The abnormalities of perception of blue are rare and their inheritance not fully investigated yet. The abnormalities of perception of red and green are not uncommon and those who have them must be excluded from work involving the recognition of signal lights; they

* The terms 'green-blindness' and 'green-weakness' are used for simplicity. When asked to match a yellow light with mixtures of red and green light, the green-blind and green-weak use too much green just as the red-blind and red-weak use too much red. But the essential abnormality in the green-blind and green-weak is complete and partial failure respectively to discriminate light with wave-lengths in the green-yellow-red range, rather than a reduction in sensitivity to green light.

are also unsuited to many branches of the dyeing, textile, paint, and printing industries. Two large scale investigations in Norway and Switzerland gave the following approximate frequencies of colour-blindness in males:

Red-blind, 1 per cent     Green-blind, 5 per cent
Red-weak, 1 per cent      Green-weak, 1·5 per cent

The total frequency of all four types in girls and women is only about 0·5 per cent.

Family investigations show that all these four conditions (and probably blue-weakness, but not blue-blindness) are determined by genes on the $X$ chromosome and show the features of sex-linked inheritance. This pattern of inheritance of colour-blindness was recognized as early as 1876. In general girls and women are rarely affected and then only if they are homozygous for one of the responsible genes. Sometimes, however, heterozygous women show a detectable degree of colour-blindness. In addition the pattern of inheritance in a number of families suggests that the genes for red-blindness and red-weakness are alleles, with the gene for red-weakness dominant to that for red-blindness. Women in these families, who from the pedigree must have the genes for red-weakness on one $X$ chromosome and the gene for red-blindness on the other $X$ chromosome, are red-weak. Using the symbol $R^b$ for the gene for red-blindness, $R^w$ for the gene for red-weakness, and $N$ for the normal gene, the genotype of these double carrier women is almost certainly as in section a of Figure 27 and not as in section b.

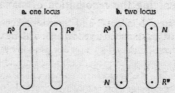

27. Inheritance of red-blindness ($R^b$) and red-weakness ($R^w$)

With genotype b one would have expected colour vision to be normal, since each gene for colour-blindness is matched by a dominant normal allele.

Similarly the genes for green-weakness and green-blindness appear to be alleles, with that for green-weakness usually dominant to that for green-blindness. But the gene-locus for the two types of defective perception of red is probably separate from that for the two types of defective perception of green. For example, in a family in Switzerland the mother was green-blind and therefore very probably homozygous for this gene; this was borne out by the finding that all her three sons were also green-blind. The father was red-blind and so

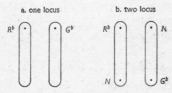

28. Inheritance of red-blindness ($R^b$) and green-blindness ($G^b$)

their daughter must have had one gene for green-blindness and one for red-blindness. This girl had no defects of colour vision suggesting, though not proving, that the genes for green- and red-blindness were not alleles and that each of them was dominated by a normal gene; the genotype of this girl is almost certainly as in section b of Figure 28 and not as in section a.

In another Swiss family in which the situation was reversed the father was green-blind and the mother red-blind. There were no sons in this family, but the two girls had normal vision though they must have carried a gene for each type of colour-blindness. Confirmation of the two loci theory may come from the sons of these girls. Normally, their sons will be either red-blind or green-blind and this will be true whether there is one locus involved, as in the preceding figure 28a, or two as in the preceding figure 28b. With 28a this must always be the case, but with 28b a crossover might occur giving a boy with normal colour vision, and the birth of such a boy would strongly support the two loci theory.

Colour-blindness is more common in whites than in other races; for example it occurs in only about 5 per cent of both Indian and Chinese males, the lowest frequency so far discovered being in Eskimoes where it is less than 1 per cent.

A possible selective advantage of colour-blindness is that men with it see animals which are hidden from normal vision by their natural camouflage. This would be useful to men such as our own Middle Stone Age ancestors, hunting in forests and woods, but valueless to the Eskimos. On the other hand, the higher incidence of colour-blindness in peoples civilized longest may merely reflect a relaxation of natural selection.

In all these characters determined by a single gene pair, blood types, plasma proteins, tasting ability, and colour vision, the connexion between the function of the gene and the characteristic observed is probably close. There is no such simple relationship between gene function and its effect on development for most ordinary physical characteristics such as eye-colour, hair form, height, and body build. The ordinary physical character where variation is perhaps nearest to being determined by a single gene pair is eye-colour, that is the colour of the iris. The iris is made up of three layers – an outer layer, always present in animals but more or less atrophied in men, a middle layer, and an inner layer. If there is no pigment in either the middle or inner layers, the iris appears pink, but this complete absence of pigment occurs only in albinos. If pigment is present in the inner layer but not in the middle layer the iris appears blue or grey. The distinction between blue and grey probably depends on the amount of atrophy of the outer layer, the greater the atrophy the more blue the eye. If pigment is present in both the inner and outer layer the iris is some shade of brown. In some peoples, for example Mongolians or Negroes, almost all the eyes are dark-brown. But in all peoples with a considerable element of north European stock there is an appreciable proportion with blue and intermediate eyes and all gradations from light-blue to dark-brown. Albinism occurs in all races, but is rare and should perhaps not be classed as a normal variation: the complete form is due to a recessive gene.

That these variations are largely genetically determined is shown by twin studies. Twins who are, on other grounds, almost certainly identical have the same eye-colour and the same detailed pattern of the iris, with the exception of the chestnut-brown flecks which are occasionally seen in the iris.

In view of this complexity of the anatomical basis of eye-colour it is unlikely that a single gene pair could be responsible for all the variations observed. It has, however, long been known that it is unusual for two blue-eyed parents to have brown-eyed children, and as early as 1907 Hurst, in England, suggested that blue-eyed individuals are homozygous for a recessive gene. The largest study of parents and children was made in Denmark in 1921 by Winge. The results are not wholly reliable as they were collected by questionnaire and not by personal observations. The parents were

Table 3. Family study of inheritance of eye-colour

| MARRIAGES | NUMBER OF CHILDREN | | |
|---|---|---|---|
| | Blue | Brown | Greyish or Bluish-green |
| Blue × Blue | 625 | 12 | 7 |
| Blue × Brown | 317 | 322 | 9 |
| Brown × Brown | 25 | 82 | – |

friends or members of two Danish natural history societies. The number of brown-eyed children born to two blue-eyed parents was less than 2 per cent, with another 1 per cent of intermediate colour. On the other hand just about one quarter of the children of two brown-eyed parents were blue-eyed. None of the studies of human eye-colour are recent, and more studies are needed. At the moment much of the observations could be explained on the certainly over-simplified hypothesis of three alleles which might be called $E^{bl}$, $E^{gr}$, and $E^{br}$, the homozygous $E^{bl}E^{bl}$ being blue-eyed, the homozygous $E^{gr}E^{gr}$ being grey-eyed, and the homozygous $E^{br}E^{br}$ being dark-brown-eyed. Heterozygotes, $E^{bl}E^{gr}$, will be grey-eyed and heterozygotes $E^{bl}E^{br}$ and $E^{gr}E^{br}$ various shades of green, hazel, and light-brown.

There are indications that a factor on the $X$ chromosome is also concerned with brown pigmentation, that in continental north European countries, but perhaps not in Britain, there is a dominant or partially dominant gene present on some of the $X$ chromosomes. Since women have two $X$ chromosomes they would be twice as likely to possess this sex-linked gene as men. The hypothesis may be tested in families. For example, on this view one would expect blue-eyed boys to have more brown-eyed sisters than brothers; both brothers and sisters of a blue-eyed boy may be brown-eyed if the mother's other $X$ chromosome carries a gene which makes for a brown eye, but sisters may also receive a brown factor in the $X$ chromosome they receive from their father. In contrast, blue-eyed girls have an equal chance of having blue-eyed brothers and sisters; the fact that they are blue-eyed shows that their father's $X$ chromosome does not carry a gene for brown eyes.

The findings in one such family study by the American, Brues, are shown in Table 4 for the brothers and sisters of the light-eyed men in the group. Dr Brues personally examined all the subjects.

Table 4. Evidence for a sex-linked gene for eye-colour

| | SIBLINGS OF LIGHT-EYED MEN | | SIBLINGS OF LIGHT-EYED WOMEN | |
| | *Brothers* % | *Sisters* % | *Brothers* % | *Sisters* % |
|---|---|---|---|---|
| Light-eyed | 64·6 | 29·9 | 57·5 | 50·7 |
| Not light-eyed | 35·4 | 70·1 | 42·5 | 49·3 |
| Number of cases | 65 | 77 | 40 | 79 |

The differences were strongly in favour of the hypothesis and supported by the families of other types. Sub-dividing the non-light eyes, Brues found that the sex-linked gene tended to produce a mixed-brown rather than a dark-brown eye. It should be noted that blue-eyed individuals will not possess this sex-linked gene and so this hypothesis does not explain the occasional brown-eyed individual born to parents who are both blue-eyed.

It is interesting to consider what are the selective advantages that have resulted in the present distribution of eye colour in the world. By far the commonest eye-colour is dark-brown, and this is also the eye-colour of the great apes. An iris with this amount of pigment has the property of preventing visible and ultra-violet light from entering the eye except through the pupil. This gives a clear image and it is probable that dark-eyed people can see better and more comfortably than the light-eyed when the light is very bright. Blue-eyed men and women often find their eyes uncomfortable in bright light, and the rare albino individuals are uncomfortable and do not see clearly even in moderate light. In cloudy, temperate zones, however, where light eyes are chiefly found, light eyes are no disadvantage. In these areas one might expect the genes for dark eyes to be gradually lost since they have no positive selective value. This would be a slow process and it is to be expected that genes for light eyes have some positive selective advantages in cloudy, temperate zones. The advantage might be indirect. For example there might be a selective advantage of a fair skin under these conditions and the genes for fair skin tend also to produce light eyes, but at the moment one can only speculate about this.

# CHAPTER 6

# *Height and Build*

## *The normal curve*

WITH the blood groups and other characters determined by a single gene pair, the variation seen in the population is discontinuous; for example, so many people are group A, so many group B, so many group O, so many group AB. With most normal variation, however, no sharp division can be recognized between one type and another. Instead there is a tendency for the population to show continuous variation from one extreme to the other, with most people fairly close to the average of the population and fewer and fewer represented as one moves in either direction towards the extremes. For many qualities that can be measured in men and women the variation follows a particular pattern of this type, known as a 'normal' curve distribution. A full account of the normal curve is given in the Pelican book *Facts from Figures* by M. J. Moroney. This curve can be described by two quantities, the arithmetical average or mean, and a measure of the variation about the average called the 'standard deviation'. About two-thirds of the population lie within one standard deviation of the mean and 95 per cent within two standard deviations of the mean.*

* The standard deviation is found by adding the squares of the individual differences from the average of the population measured, dividing this figure by one less than the number of people measured, and taking the square root. In algebraic form

$$s = \sqrt{\frac{\varSigma (x - \bar{x})^2}{n-1}}$$

where s is the standard deviation, $\varSigma$ indicates 'the sum of', x is the individual measurement, $\bar{x}$ is the arithmetic mean of the measurements,

*Inheritance of height*

Height is used in the next few sections to illustrate the principles of inheritance of normally distributed qualities. Other characters, such as counts of the ridges seen in finger-prints, have been more thoroughly investigated and are more completely genetically determined, but would be less familiar to most readers.

A distribution curve for height which has an average of 68 inches and standard deviations of 2·6 inches is shown in Figure 29. This corresponds with the distribution of height

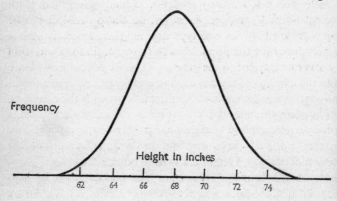

Frequency

Height in inches

62　64　66　68　70　72　74

29. A distribution curve for height in full-grown men in south-east England

in fully-grown young men in south-east England, which is the region with the tallest men in the British Isles. About

---

and n is the number of individuals measured. The standard deviation squared, that is

$$\frac{\Sigma (x-\bar{x})^2}{n-1}$$

is known as the 'variance'. These squared deviations have many useful properties mathematically, which the unsquared deviations do not.

wo thirds of the population will lie within one standard
eviation on either side of the mean (in this example be-
ween 65·4 and 70·6 inches), while only about 1 in 20
vill be beyond two standards from the mean (in this
xample 1 in 40 less than 62·8 inches and 1 in 40 more than
3·2 inches).

## A theoretical model for the inheritance of height

t so happens that a normal distribution of this kind is just
vhat one would expect to find in a population for a charac-
eristic the variation of which is due to a number of causes
ach of small effect. This is true whether these causes are
genetic or environmental. If genetic endowment for the
levelopment of a quality such as height were determined by
ust a few gene pairs, this would produce a normal distribution. For example, let us first suppose that a single gene
pair is concerned, for which there is one common form of
he gene which we will call $H$, with a gene frequency of $\frac{1}{2}$,
nd two alternative forms $h_1$ and $h_2$, each with a frequency
of only $\frac{1}{4}$. Further, let us suppose that while $H$ tends to pro-
luce an average height of 68 inches, $h_1$ increases height by
: inches, and $h_2$ reduces it by 2 inches. Then the distribution
of heights in the population would be given by the algebraic
xpression $(\frac{1}{4}h_1 + \frac{1}{2}H + \frac{1}{4}h_2)^2$ or by the chequer-board dia-
ram shown in Figure 30.

This shows one-sixteenth of the population at each of the
xtremes of 64 and 72 inches, four-sixteenths or one quarter
t each of the intermediate heights of 66 and 70 inches, and
ix-sixteenths or three-eighths at the average height of 68
nches. This distribution is shown in Figure 31.

The distribution is still discontinuous but it shows some-
hing approaching a normal curve with standard deviation
ust over 2 inches.

It is only necessary to add another pair of genes control-
ng height with similar alleles $t_1$, $T$, and $t_2$ (adding $+2, 0,$ and

T – D

| | *Alleles on one chromosome* | | |
|---|---|---|---|
| | $(\frac{1}{4})h_1$ +2 | $(\frac{1}{2})H$ 0 | $(\frac{1}{2})h_2$ −2 |
| $(\frac{1}{4})h_1$ +2 | $(\frac{1}{16})$ 72 | $(\frac{1}{8})$ 70 | $(\frac{1}{16})$ 68 |
| $(\frac{1}{2})H$ 0 | $(\frac{1}{8})$ 70 | $(\frac{1}{4})$ 68 | $(\frac{1}{8})$ 66 |
| $(\frac{1}{4})h_2$ −2 | $(\frac{1}{16})$ 68 | $(\frac{1}{8})$ 66 | $(\frac{1}{16})$ 64 |

*Alleles on the other chromosome*

30. The genotypes for height produced by 3 alleles at a single gene locus

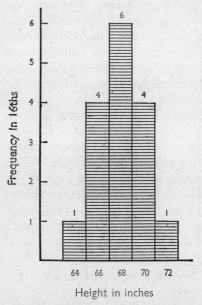

31. The distribution of height produced by 3 alleles at a single gene locus

—2 inches respectively), and to allow a small variation due to environmental factors to get something very close to a normal distribution. The distribution of genetic endowment from two such gene-loci can, once again, be worked out by a chequer-board diagram. The variation due to one gene pair is put along one axis and that due to the other gene pair along the other axis. Alternatively, it can be worked out algebraically by expanding the expression $(\frac{1}{4}h_1 + \frac{1}{2}H + \frac{1}{4}h_2)^2 (\frac{1}{4}t_2 + \frac{1}{2}T + \frac{1}{4}t_2)^2$. The distribution so formed is shown in Figure 32.

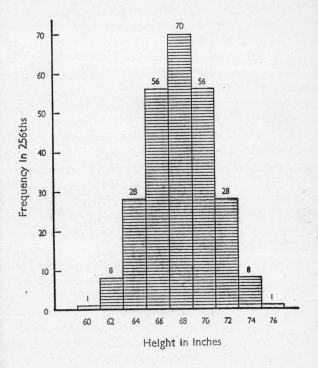

32. The distribution of height produced by 3 alleles at each of two gene loci

This distribution is once again discontinuous, but it is now close to a normal curve with an arithmetical average of 68 inches and standard deviation of 2·8 inches, and so approximates quite closely to the actual distribution of height of young men in south-east England.

The true mechanism of the inheritance of height is almost certainly not so simple as this; but the illustration given shows how readily quite simple genetic hypotheses will account for nearly continuous, normal distributions. Even a single gene pair with several alternative forms of the gene, instead of the two postulated above, would give a nearly normal distribution. We know, however, that more than one gene pair is concerned with height since a single gene pair would mean that only four alleles could be present in a man and his wife, and only four genetic endowments for height could occur in their children. In practice it is found that brothers and sisters can show much more variety than this. It is also the case that the existence of a normal distribution for a character in the population does not necessarily mean that genetic factors are concerned; numerous environmental factors determining height might also give a normal distribution. The extent to which height is genetically determined has to be investigated in the usual way by twin and family studies.

## Height in twins

Twin studies indicate that adult height is largely genetically determined, except where illness has actually deformed skeletal structure. The degree of resemblance between identical twins brought up together is high: when the twins are full grown, differences of more than 1 inch, that is about 1·5 per cent, are unusual. Newman, Freeman, and Holzinger found that the resemblance was still high in their nineteen pairs of identical twins brought up apart and so experiencing differing environments. Their findings are shown in Table 5.

Table 5. The resemblance for height of nineteen identical pairs
of twins brought up apart

| ADULTS | | CHILDREN | |
|---|---|---|---|
| *Height difference* (in inches) | *Number of pairs* | *Height difference* (in inches) | *Number of pairs* |
| 0 – ½ | 10 | 0 – ½ | 1 |
| ½ – 1 | 4 | ½ – 1 | 0 |
| 1 – 1½ | 1 | 1 – 1½ | 2 |
| more than 1½ | 0 | more than 1½ | 1 |

The adult differences are no more than for identical twins
reared together and much less than between fraternal twins
reared together.

*Effect of nutrition on height in children and adults*

The height of children, in contrast to that of adults, appears
to be much more under the influence of environmental factors, such as nutrition. The one twin pair in Table 5 who
differed by more than 1·5 inch in height were eleven and a
half years old. There has been an increase in the average
height of the eleven-year-old London County Council school
child of about 4 inches since the turn of the century. But
over the same period it is a matter of dispute whether there
has been any increase at all in the height of the fully adult
Englishman or woman of the age of twenty-five. If there has
been any increase it is only of the order of 1 inch. What
environmental improvements appear to be doing is, in the
main, to accelerate growth, so that full adult height is being
reached earlier. Puberty is being reached at a steadily
younger age in both boys and girls and almost full adult
height in men is being reached on the average at eighteen or
nineteen years of age, while fifty years ago this was true only
of men in the most favoured social classes.

There are differences still in the height of men and women

in the different social classes, but much of this is probably
genetically rather than environmentally determined and may
be due to a small but definite association between height and
intelligence. This is indicated, for example, by the findings
in a recent survey by the Department of Social Medicine at
Oxford. Middle-class children, it was found, are on the
average taller than working-class children. But working-
class children who are selected for grammar-school education are, on the average, taller than working-class children
who are not selected, and taller too than middle-class
children who are not selected. Similarly, in Aberdeen recently, it was found that young women of working-class
origin who marry young men in middle-class occupations
are on the average taller than the remainder of their group.
They are also taller than girls of middle-class origin who
marry young men with working-class occupations. Some of
the claims that the average height of fully-adult British men
has increased can, in part at least, be explained by earlier
maturity, for example, in the case of service recruits; some
can be explained by intelligence and social class differences,
for example, when the height of undergraduates is compared
with that of their often working-class fathers.

Other claims for an increase in height can be explained by
the well-established fact that men and women who migrate
from their place of birth tend to be taller (and more intelligent) than those who are not so mobile. Records from the
armed services, the prisons, and anthropological surveys
suggest that full adult height has not changed by more than
one and a half inches for the past century. Estimates of
stature in early periods have to be based on skeletal remains.
These are often scanty and the series may be to some extent
unrepresentative. But they suggest that there has been little
appreciable change in height in Britain over the past 5,000
years, and probably little change for a much longer time
still. Estimated average height for men of the Old Stone Age

western Europe is 69 inches, in Britain in the New Stone Age 66 inches, in the Bronze Age 68 inches, in the Iron-Age Celts 66 inches, in Anglo-Saxons 67 inches, in the Middle Ages 66 inches, and at the present time from 67 to 68 inches in different parts of the country. It would seem that not only is adult height largely genetically determined, but that the natural selective forces operating on height must have been fairly constant over the last 5,000 years.

## Studies of the inheritance of height from fathers to sons

The earliest systematic family studies of the inheritance of height are due to Galton, and his successor Pearson, at University College in London. It is regrettable that no similar study has been made in the last fifty years. Galton and Pearson compared the heights of fathers and sons, and of pairs of brothers. They found that the sons of tall men tended to be tall, but not so tall as their fathers, and the sons of short men tended to be short, but not so short as their fathers. In each case the sons showed considerable variation in their height, but their average tended to be half-way back towards the average height of the general population. This is shown in Figure 33.

The true relationship is shown as a continuous line, the line of no relationship is shown in unequal dashes, and the line of complete resemblance is shown in equal dashes. The true line lies half-way between the other two. Galton coined the term 'regression' for this tendency of son's height to 'regress' half-way back towards the mean of the population from the height of his father.*

This regression to the mean by half is just what one would expect in multifactorial inheritance, provided that the action

* Galton's 'ratio of regression' and the modern 'regression coefficient', however, measure the proportion in which sons, on the average, are less exceptional than their fathers. So a regression towards the mean of three-quarters means that the 'regression coefficient' is one quarter.

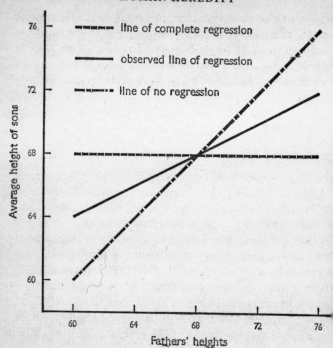

33. Regression towards the mean of son's height on father's height

of the genes is additive, without dominance, and provided
that there is no tendency for tall men to marry tall women
and short men to marry short women. With multifactorial
inheritance a tall father, transmitting only one of each of his
23 chromosome pairs to his son, will on the average transmit
only half the genes which made him exceptional. The
mother's contribution, if there is no tendency for like to
marry like, will be centred on the average, and so the son's
height will tend to be half-way between that of his exceptional
father and the average. This is readily seen if we presume
again that a single gene pair controls height with alleles *H*,

$h_1$, and $h_2$, of which $H$ has a frequency of one half and tends to the production of average height, $h_1$ has a frequency of one quarter and tends to increase height by 2 inches, and $h_2$ has a frequency of one quarter and tends to reduce height by 2 inches. The tallest men on this system would be 72 inches tall, having the genotype $h_1h_1$. The distribution of height of their sons can be read from Figure 34. The sons

|  | Mother's chromosome | | |
|---|---|---|---|
|  | $(\frac{1}{4})h_1$ +2 | $(\frac{1}{2})H$ 0 | $(\frac{1}{4})h_2$ −2 |
| $h_1$ +2 | $(\frac{1}{4})$ 72 | $(\frac{1}{2})$ 70 | $(\frac{1}{4})$ 68 |

34. Heights of sons of 72-inch tall fathers on the one gene locus theory

average 70 inches, half of them being this height, a quarter are as tall as the father, and a quarter the average height of the general population. In the same way fathers of height 70 inches would on this simple hypothesis have the genotype $h_1H$ and their sons have the heights shown in Figure 35.

|  | Mother's chromosome | | |
|---|---|---|---|
|  | $(\frac{1}{4}) h_1$ +2 | $(\frac{1}{2})H$ 0 | $(\frac{1}{4})h_2$ −2 |
| $(\frac{1}{2})h_1$ +2 | $(\frac{1}{8})$ 72 | $(\frac{1}{4})$ 70 | $(\frac{1}{8})$ 68 |
| $(\frac{1}{2})H$ 0 | $(\frac{1}{8})$ 70 | $(\frac{1}{4})$ 68 | $(\frac{1}{8})$ 66 |

35. Heights of sons of 70-inch tall fathers on the one gene locus theory

The sons have the distribution one-eighth 66 inches, three-eighths 68 inches, three-eighths 70 inches, and one-eighth 72 inches. It is worth noticing that one son in eight in this group is taller than his tall father and another one in eight is shorter than the average of the population.

The effect of many gene pairs behaving in the same way would be to produce a range of sons' heights normally distributed about an average half-way between that of the fathers and the general population. The same relationship will hold between the heights of mothers and daughters and also, if due allowance is made for sex differences, between mothers and sons, always assuming that there is no tendency for like to marry like, and that the effects of the gene for height are additive.

It is important to note, as Galton did, that the tendency for sons' heights to regress half-way to the mean from fathers' heights does not imply any reduction in the variation of height in the next generation. This variation depends essentially on the gene frequency, somewhat modified by the amount of assortative mating. Neglecting for a moment the small amount of assortative mating for height, and taking again the simple model of three alleles $H$, $h_1$, and $h_2$ controlling height, the distribution of height in both fathers' and sons' generations will be as in Figure 32. The resultant relationship between fathers' heights and sons' heights is as in Figure 36. The sons' heights and their frequencies are shown in the squares of the chequer-board and also in the histograms.

From this it can be seen that the distribution of sons' heights is like the fathers', one-sixteenth at 72 inches, four-sixteenths at 70 inches, six-sixteenths at 68 inches, four-sixteenths at 66 inches, and one-sixteenth at 64 inches. It can also be seen that only one-quarter of the tallest, 72-inch sons are born to the tallest fathers, the moderately tall 70-inch fathers provide one half of the tallest sons, and the other quarter are the

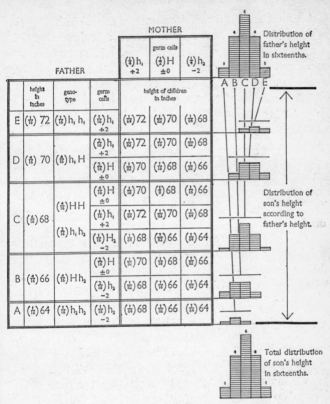

36. The constancy of the distribution of height from one generation to another despite filial regression

exceptional sons of average fathers. Only one son in twenty-four born to average fathers would be 72 inches tall on this model, but since average fathers are the most numerous group they contribute one in four of the tallest sons, and also one in four of the shortest sons.

The regression to the mean applies from exceptional sons to their fathers, as well as from exceptional fathers to sons.

The average height of the fathers of 72-inch sons is $\frac{1}{4}(72 + 70 + 70 + 68)$ or 70 inches. Similarly, the average height of the fathers of 64-inch sons is $\frac{1}{4}(64 + 66 + 66 + 68)$ or 66 inches.

## Effect, in theory, of assortative marriage on the resemblance of fathers and sons

In so far as there is a tendency for like to marry like, on a simple additive multifactorial theory for the inheritance of height, one would expect less regression to the average of the population. One would expect instead that sons' heights would be distributed about a point mid-way between those of the exceptional fathers and those of the mothers, when the mother's height has been converted into its masculine equivalent.* For example, if, when fathers were 72 inches tall mothers on the average were 66 inches tall – which is about equivalent to a man just under 72 inches – one would expect no regression towards the average of the population and the sons to average 72 inches tall. Again, if fathers of 72 inches married women equivalent to men of 70 inches, the sons would average 71 inches tall. The regression in this case is only a quarter of the way back to the average of the population instead of the regression of a half that takes place when there is no assortative marriage for height. There are no recent studies of the amount of assortative marriage for height. A small degree probably occurs, though much less than, say, for intelligence, and this will tend to reduce the regression towards the average of sons' height from fathers' height.

## Effect of dominance on the resemblance between fathers and sons

The assumption we have been making that the effect of the

* Galton observed that this conversion might be made by adding 1 inch for every foot of a woman's height.

gene is additive and that there is no dominance or recessiveness between the alternative forms of gene is probably also incorrect. There is a distinct suggestion, for example, that certain genes for shortness are dominant to genes for tallness. One investigator in America, Davenport, found that it was more common for two short parents to have a tall child than it was for two tall parents to have a short child. This suggests that some short individuals may be heterozygous for partially recessive genes for tallness which do not affect their own height much, but which may affect any of their children who are homozygous for such genes. Understandably, the effect of such dominance would be to increase the regression to the mean of heights of sons from their fathers' heights. The findings at University College that the regression is close to half may well be due to the effect of assortative marriage and dominance about cancelling each other.

The amount of the effect of dominance depends on the relative frequency of the dominant and recessive alternative genes. Where they both have a frequency of one half the regression to the mean, from this gene-locus, becomes two-thirds. This may be seen if we imagine a pair of alleles controlling height, $H$ and $h$, each with a frequency of one half $H$ being dominant to $h$, and effects such that homozygous $HH$ (one quarter of the population) and heterozygous $Hh$ (one half of the population) are 1 inch below average height, and homozygous $hh$ (one quarter of the population) are 3 inches above average height. If the average height is 68 inches the population would then consist of three-quarters who were short men of height 67 inches and one-quarter tall men of height 71 inches. The relation between sons' height and fathers' height, assuming no assortative marriage, may be seen from Figure 37.

The average height of the sons of the 71-inch tall fathers is seen to be 69 inches and the average height of the sons of the 67-inch short fathers is seen to be $67\frac{2}{3}$ inches; in each case the

*Father's height and genotype*

|  | $(\frac{1}{4})hh$ 71 | $(\frac{1}{2})Hh$ 67 | $(\frac{1}{4})HH$ 67 |
|---|---|---|---|
| $(\frac{1}{2})h$ | $(\frac{1}{8})$ 71 | $(\frac{1}{8})$ 67  $(\frac{1}{8})$ 71 | $(\frac{1}{8})$ 67 |
| $(\frac{1}{2})H$ | $(\frac{1}{8})$ 67 | $(\frac{1}{4})$ 67 | $(\frac{1}{8})$ 67 |
| Average of sons' heights | $(\frac{1}{4})$ 69 | $(\frac{1}{2})$ 68 | $(\frac{1}{4})$ 67 |
|  |  | $(\frac{3}{4})$ $67\frac{2}{3}$ | |

*Mother's germ cells*

37. Relation between sons' heights and fathers'
heights with dominance at a single gene locus

regression to the mean is two-thirds. The same relationships
apply if several gene pairs are behaving in the same way. For
example, let us imagine a second similar gene pair $T$ and $t$,
but in which the recessive homozygote genotype $tt$ reduced
height to 3 inches below the average, while $TT$ and $Tt$ were
an inch above the average. This would, in combination with
the first pair, give a population of men with a symmetrical
distribution for height – three-sixteenths at 72 inches, ten-
sixteenths at 68 inches, and three-sixteenths at 64 inches, as
shown in Figure 38.

With no assortative marriage the average height of the sons
of 72-inch fathers would be $69\frac{1}{3}$ inches as may be seen from
Figure 39, one third of the tall fathers having genotype
$hhTT$ and two thirds genotype $hhTt$, thus two thirds of their
germ cells being of type $hT$ and one third of type $ht$.

Similarly the average height of the sons of the short fathers
of height 64 inches will be $66\frac{2}{3}$ inches. In each case the regression towards the average of 68 inches is two-thirds.

If the frequency of the dominant gene is, however, not

*One gene pair*

|  |  | $(\frac{1}{4})hh$ +3 | $(\frac{1}{2})Hh$ −1 | $(\frac{1}{4})HH$ −1 |
|---|---|---|---|---|
| *Other gene pair* | $(\frac{1}{4})TT$ +1 | $(\frac{1}{16})$ 72 | $(\frac{1}{8})$ 68 | $(\frac{1}{16})$ 68 |
|  | $(\frac{1}{2})Tt$ +1 | $(\frac{1}{8})$ 72 | $(\frac{1}{4})$ 68 | $(\frac{1}{8})$ 68 |
|  | $(\frac{1}{4})tt$ −3 | $(\frac{1}{16})$ 68 | $(\frac{1}{8})$ 64 | $(\frac{1}{16})$ 64 |

38. The genotypes for height on a two gene
    locus theory, with dominance

*Germ cells of tall fathers*

|  |  | $(\frac{2}{3})hT$ | $(\frac{1}{3})ht$ |
|---|---|---|---|
| *Mother's germ cells* | $(\frac{1}{4})hT$ | $(\frac{1}{6})$ 72 | $(\frac{1}{12})$ 72 |
|  | $(\frac{1}{4})ht$ | $(\frac{1}{6})$ 72 | $(\frac{1}{12})$ 68 |
|  | $(\frac{1}{4})HT$ | $(\frac{1}{6})$ 68 | $(\frac{1}{12})$ 68 |
|  | $(\frac{1}{4})Ht$ | $(\frac{1}{6})$ 68 | $(\frac{1}{12})$ 64 |

39. The heights of sons of tall
    fathers on the two gene locus
    theory, with dominance

one half but very low, it will have little effect on regression. Apart from assortative marriage, it will be most unusual for both parents to possess the gene. If only the father has the gene and so is exceptional because of it, he has a one half chance of passing it to his son, so that the effect of a rare dominant gene on the regression of son on father will be to tend to make it the usual half. On the other hand, if the dominant gene is very common, the exceptional fathers will be those who have the recessive gene for each member of this particular gene pair. Such a father will always transmit one such gene to his son, but the gene from the mother, apart from assortative marriage, will nearly always be the much commoner dominant gene and in that case there is no resemblance between father and son. The effect, then, of a gene pair with a very high frequency of the dominant gene is to produce no resemblance between father and son, that is to say complete regression to the average of the population.

## Regression of children's height from mid-parental height

It is worth noting that with simple additive multifactorial inheritance there is no regression of the average height of children from mid-parental height towards the average of the population. There is a simple one to one linear relationship, and the distribution of children's height is centred round the mid-parental height if correction is made for sex differences. But the regression of mid-parental height from child's height is one half, and the correlation coefficient between mid-parental height and child's height is the square root of one multiplied by a half, that is 0·71. The effect of dominance is to increase the regression from mid-parental height to child's height and also to make the relationship non-linear. For example, on the two alleles at one gene-locus hypothesis; the offspring of two tall $hh$ parents will all be equally tall; the offspring of short $HH \times HH$ and $HH \times Hh$ (also short) parents will be equally short; but the offspring of short $Hh \times Hh$ parents will be three-quarters short and one-quarter tall, and so on the average the children show regression towards the mean.

## Resemblance between other pairs of relatives from multi-factorial inheritance

The relationships between other types of relatives on simple additive multifactorial inheritance depend on the number of genes they are likely to have in common by virtue of their relationship. A father and son have, apart from the genes on the $X$ chromosome, half of their genes in common because of the relationship. A pair of brothers need not have half their genes in common, but will do so on the average, since, for each chromosome pair of their two parents, it is an even chance whether the brothers get the same chromosome or a different one. They may have more than half their genes in common and they may have fewer, but the deviations will tend to be equal on each side of a half and the average will tend to be a half. One would, therefore, expect to find the relationship between brothers is much the same as that for father and son. For height this is found to be so in practice. Pearson and later investigators found that the regression of the height of the brothers of exceptionally tall or exceptionally short men tends to be half-way back to that of the average of the general population. The same is true of pairs of sisters and of sister and brother when allowance is made for sex difference in height.

Relatives such as nephew and uncle have, on the average, one quarter of their genes in common because of their relationship. If a man has a particular gene, there is a half chance that a particular brother or sister also has it and a further half chance – a quarter in all – that his brother or sister will transmit it to a son. With simple additive multifactorial inheritance one would expect to find that, starting with tall uncles, the average height of their nephews would be three-quarters of the way back to the average of the population. Besides uncle–nephew, aunt–niece, uncle–niece, and aunt–nephew, other relatives who have, on the average, a quarter of their genes in common because of the relationship are half-brothers and sisters, grandparent–grandchild, and double first cousins (a pair of children are double first cousins when they are first cousins both through their mothers and their fathers).

*Effect of assortative marriage on the resemblance of brothers*

These resemblances, like those between parent and child, will be modified by dominance and the tendency for assortative marriage. For example, on the simple hypothesis of genes $H$, $h_1$, and $h_2$ with frequencies of one half, one quarter, and one quarter respectively, and $h_1$ increasing and $h_2$ reducing height by 2 inches, a tall man has the genetic constitution $h_1h_1$. His brother has a half chance of inheriting the same $h_1$ gene from each parent; the remaining half chance for the other gene from each parent if there is no assortative marriage is $H$ or $h_1$, or $h_2$, with probabilities of one quarter, one eighth, and one eighth respectively. The probabilities of each type of brother are shown in Figure 40.

|  |  | *One chromosome* | | |
|---|---|---|---|---|
| | | $(\frac{1}{2} + \frac{1}{8})h_1$ $+2$ | $(\frac{1}{4})H$ $0$ | $(\frac{1}{8})h_2$ $-2$ |
| *Other chromosome* | $(\frac{1}{2} + \frac{1}{8})h_1$ $+2$ | $(\frac{25}{64})$ 72 | $(\frac{5}{32})$ 70 | $(\frac{5}{64})$ 68 |
| | $(\frac{1}{4})H$ $0$ | $(\frac{5}{32})$ 70 | $(\frac{1}{16})$ 68 | $(\frac{1}{32})$ 66 |
| | $(\frac{1}{8})h_2$ $-2$ | $(\frac{5}{64})$ 68 | $(\frac{1}{32})$ 66 | $(\frac{1}{64})$ 64 |

40. The heights of brothers of tall men on the one gene locus theory

The diagram shows that 25/64 would be 72 inches tall, 20/64 would be 70 inches tall, 14/64 would be 68 inches tall, 4/64 would be 66 inches tall, and 1/64 would be 64 inches tall; the average height would be 70 inches and the regression half-way back to the mean. With assortative marriage the regression to the mean will be decreased. It will still be true that the brothers of tall $h_1h_1$ individuals will have a half chance of having $h_1$ on each chromosome in virtue of the relationship; but because of the assortative marriage the additional chance of getting $h_1$ from either parent is more than an eighth. The effect is similar to that on the regression of father to son but is somewhat complicated, increasing with the number of generations in which assortative marriage has operated, and it cannot be demonstrated simply.

## Effect of dominance on the resemblance of brothers

The effect of dominance on the resemblance between brothers will be to increase the amount of regression to the mean but not quite to the same extent as with father and son. For example, where the dominant gene is very rare and a man is exceptional because of it, his brother has a half chance of sharing this gene and is most unlikely to receive another gene of the same kind. As with father and son, the effect will be towards making regression half and so there will be little effect of the dominance on the usual regression. But if the dominant gene is very common, then an exceptional man is homozygous for the rare recessive allele and his brother would have a one in four chance of having both these genes. The effect would be to make regression 0·75 (or a three-quarters), and not 1·0 as with father and son. When the dominant and the recessive genes each have a frequency of half and, for example, the tall individuals have the genotype $hh$ and a height of 71 inches (and the short $hH$ or $HH$ and a height of 67 inches) then the brothers of these tall men will have a half chance of receiving the gene $h$ from each

parent because of the relationship. The distribution of the
brothers' heights can be seen from Figure 41. Thus nine-

| | *One germ cell* | |
|---|---|---|
| | $(\frac{3}{4})h$ | $(\frac{1}{4})H$ |
| $(\frac{3}{4})h$ | $(\frac{9}{16})$　71 | $(\frac{3}{16})$　67 |
| $(\frac{1}{4})H$ | $(\frac{3}{16})$　67 | $(\frac{1}{16})$　67 |

*Other germ cell*

41. The distribution of height of
brothers of tall men with dominance

sixteenths will be tall and seven-sixteenths short, the average will be $69\frac{1}{4}$ inches, and the regression back to the mean
is seven-twelfths or 0·58. This may be compared with the
regression of two-thirds or 0·67 which the same pair of
genes would produce on the regression of sons' height from
fathers' height. In fact, the regression to the mean found for
brothers for height is close to a half and it may well be, as
suggested for the father–son relationship, that there is some
element of dominance balancing some degree of assortative
marriage.

### The age of onset of genetic influence on height

The weight or height of a baby at birth appears to be un-
influenced by its genetic constitution. There is a relation to
mother's height, but this appears to be non-genetic. The
reasons for believing this are: there is little relationship
between a baby's length at birth and his ultimate height;
half-brothers and sisters with the same father show no
resemblance in birth weight, in contrast to half-brothers

and sisters with the same mother; first cousins whose fathers are brothers or who are related through a brother and sister show no resemblance in birth weight, in contrast to cousins whose mothers are sisters.

By the age of three however, there are indications that the genetic constitution for height is taking effect since there is a strong relation between length at this age and adult height. In a recent study by Tanner and his colleagues in which a number of adult men and women were measured who had also been carefully measured for the first five years of their lives by Professor Low in Aberdeen, it was found that the formulae which gave the best predictions of adult height were:

Men – adult height (in inches) $= 1 \cdot 27 \times$ length at age three (in inches) $+ 21 \cdot 0$.

Women – adult height (in inches) $= 1 \cdot 29 \times$ length at age three (in inches) $+ 16 \cdot 1$.

But Tanner notes that because of the tendency for earlier maturity, mentioned above, these formulae probably give too high predictions if applied to present-day children. In individual cases this formula may predict heights up to 2 inches above or below the height actually attained.

From age three until about the onset of puberty, growth is fairly steady in that most children will move up in much the same relation to their fellows; a child that is about one standard deviation above the average will, in most instances, remain in this position and, although no figures are available yet, it is probable that height at age three would predict height at age ten very accurately.

At puberty, however, there is always a spurt in growth, and growth in height usually slows almost to a standstill about four and a half years after the start of this spurt. The age at onset of the spurt is an important factor in deciding adult height: the child who starts a spurt early from an average height for his or her age will tend to be short; a child who starts late will tend to be tall. The age of onset of the spurt and of puberty is in part under genetic control, as shown for example in girls by the greater correspondence of the age of onset of menstruation in identical than in fraternal twins, and there is a suggestion that these genes are independent of those controlling height in early childhood. This has not yet, however, been fully studied. There are also variations in the amount of the puberty spurt which have not yet been studied genetically; though it will be surprising if twin studies do not show here, too, evidence of genetic control.

The time of onset of puberty is a reflection of the child's maturity. A child who is going to reach puberty early may be recognized at any age from three onwards by taking X-ray pictures of the skeleton; the wrist is particularly suitable. His bony development, in the sense that bone has replaced cartilage, is in advance of the average. It is found that the resemblance between pairs of brothers and pairs of sisters in childhood for height is increased to about the level of a regression to the mean of one half, if allowance is made for difference in maturity. Without such allowances the regression to the mean is nearer to two-thirds than one half.

Therefore, when children's heights are compared with the heights of their parents, it is to be expected that the resemblance will increase as the child grows older and genes affecting growth successively exert their influence. A small-scale but careful study by Bayley in California relating boys' height to the mid-height of the two parents (mother's height corrected for sex) is illustrated in Figure 42. It can be seen from this diagram that the correlation rose from under $0 \cdot 3$ in infancy to about $0 \cdot 7$ in the late teens. The maximum correlation expected from multifactorial inheritance with mid-parental height is $0 \cdot 71$; this corresponds with no regression towards the mean of child's height from mid-parental height, but a regression towards the mean of 0·5 of mid-parental height from child's height.

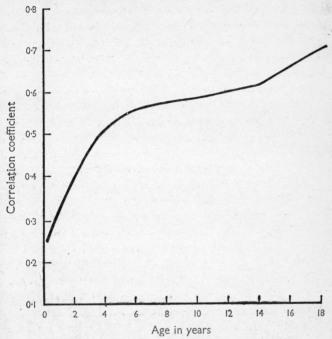

42. Resemblance of boys' heights to mid-parental height (after Bayley)

## Inheritance of body-build

The inheritance of body-build is of interest because there are indications that body-build is more related both to mental qualities and susceptibility to certain diseases than is height. The tendency of men of lean linear build to be intense and intellectual in temperament, in contrast to the cheerfulness and sociability of plump, broad individuals was well known to Shakespeare and no doubt much earlier too. It is also obvious, looking at pairs of identical twins, and parents and their children, that body-build is quite strongly inherited. Genetic study has, however, been held up by lack of agreement on how body-build should be measured. One factor in body-build is the relationship of the length of the bony skeleton to its breadth, length being measured by height or, almost as well, by the length of some of the long bones such as the shin bone or the upper-arm bone, while breadth is measured by the bony width of the shoulders or the hips. The genetics of this 'linearity factor' have not been fully studied.

Other factors in body-build are those which determine the amount of muscle and fat. The thickness of muscle and fat is fairly constant in different parts of the body so that it can be measured, for example, by taking X-ray photographs of accessible parts of the body, such as the upper arm or the calf, where bone muscle and fat may be distinguished. The Oxford Department of Social Medicine has recently reported measurements of bone, muscle, and fat in young children up to the age of five years and their brothers and sisters. It was found that the amount of bone, muscle, and fat are quite independent of each other and so inherited independently and that there are marked resemblances between brothers and between sisters and between brother–sister pairs when correction is made for age. The regressions to the mean are less even than half, after the age of three, for muscle and bone and about half for fat. Fat is, of course, much more influenced by diet. The finding that regression to the average is less than half for bone and muscle could be due both to a tendency for the parents to resemble each other and to common family environment.

## Natural selection and height

The average adult height of the races of man is, with few exceptions, between 62 and 70 inches for men and 4 to 6 inches shorter for women. The range of average height has been constant for a very long time and antedates the evolution of our own species. The first fully erect and bipedal man-apes, the Australopithecines of South Africa living about a million years ago, were, on the average, considerably shorter than this, some species perhaps averaging as little as 48 inches. By about a quarter of a million years ago, however, the early men of *Homo erectus* type from Java and China were already of about the same height and build as modern man, and there has been no major change since in these characters, though there have been great developments in other characters such as an increase of brain size and a decrease in size of jaws and teeth.

An adult height of 62 to 70 inches has therefore, on balance, presumably selective advantages over heights above or below this level. There are several disadvantages of shortness and generally small body size, but the disadvantages of tallness and generally large body size are not so obvious. One to which attention has been drawn by Haldane is that, generally speaking, weight is proportional to the cube of an animal's height, while the active strength of muscle and the passive strength of bone is proportional to the square of height. Accordingly, the legs of an elephant or rhinoceros have to be massive in relation to its body size, in comparison with the legs of a mouse and, even more, of an ant. In an activity demanding both strength and speed, such as boxing, men of about 71 inches and 13 stone can hold their own against bigger men, and on several occasions the world heavy-weight championship has been held by men who weighed only $12\frac{1}{2}$ stone and who were natural light heavy-weights. In activities demanding endurance of wind and limb, such as marathon running, men of about 67 inches and 9 to 10 stone can, in general, more than hold their own against taller and heavier men.

Within the general limits of physical efficiency there will be regional variations in selective forces, though we are far from being able to explain all the racial differences in height and body-build. Within Europe in general, the races living in colder climates are more heavily built. This physique has advantages in minimizing heat loss since it exposes less skin surface. The largest and heaviest element in the British Isles is thought to be the descendants of the Old Stone Age population of Ice Age Europe, most strongly represented now in the west of Ireland and the Scottish Highlands. The darker and more lightly-built element now best represented in north Wales and the north-east counties of England is thought to be derived from Neolithic immigrants from the warm countries bordering the Mediterranean. The Iron Age immigrants appear closest to the present-day British averages, while the preceding Bronze Age and subsequent Anglo-Saxon immigrants were somewhat more heavily built and are thought to have contained more of the Old Stone Age strain.

Cold due to high altitude has the same effect as distance from the Equator, and mountain dwellers from all parts of the world, the Alps in Europe, the Himalayas in India, and the highlands in Japan, tend to be heavily built. In contrast, dwellers in hot dry climates, for example in desert regions of North Africa and Australia, tend to be lightly built, with a large surface of skin in relation to their height and weight. A small direct effect of environment cannot yet be excluded, but probably the major part of these differences is genetically determined.

# CHAPTER 7

# Intelligence

## Inheritance of intelligence

THE idea that intelligence varies from one individual to another and that this is in part inherited is old, but has only recently been investigated methodically. Galton put forward the proposition that there is a general mental capacity and that it is inherited. He noted that many men of great achievement in intellectual professions, such as the Law, Science, and Literature, had succeeded in spite of severe environmental handicaps. It was probable, therefore, that their exceptional gifts were in part innate. He also estimated the proportion of relatives of outstandingly capable men who were themselves eminent and he published his findings in a book entitled *Hereditary Genius* in 1869.

Galton's findings were that the number of male first degree relations, that is fathers, sons, and brothers, of eminent men who were also eminent was as high as a quarter; many of the female relations of the same degree were also eminent. He thought it unlikely that this high proportion could be explained entirely by familial and cultural advantages; it was enormously higher than the proportion of men and women of similar education and social status who became eminent. Further, Galton noted that the proportion of eminent relations fell off sharply as one reached the second degree male relations of eminent men, that is grandfathers, grandsons, and uncles, although the proportion here was still much above the proportion one might expect by chance. By the time one reached the fourth degree relations, however, there was little remarkable about them. This sharp falling off, Galton suggested, is just what one would expect if inheritance is concerned, but would not be expected to the same degree if the familial resemblances were environmental.

Both Galton's propositions have since been challenged. In particular the American, Thorndike, has championed the view that there is no such quality as general ability, only a number of special abilities. The controversy continues, but most modern authorities, for example Valentine in his Pelican book *The Normal Child* and Eysenck in his Pelican book *Uses and Abuses of Psychology*, believe that there is such a thing as 'general ability' which is of major importance. They also believe, however, that there are 'special abilities', such as verbal ability, ability for dealing with numbers, spatial ability, and musical ability. The general ability is close to that which we ordinarily think of as 'reasoning ability'.

The other hypothesis, that general intelligence is to some degree inherited, has been challenged, perhaps chiefly for emotional and political reasons. Some educational enthusiasts have been afraid that the viewpoint that there are variations in innate intelligence which are inherited may lead to the withdrawal of educational opportunity for children in certain social classes or of certain races. In addition some unsophisticated men and women have thought that variation in intelligence must be *either* environmental *or* genetic, and so, having shown that some of the variation is environmental, consider that they have proved that there is no genetic variation.

## Measurement of intelligence

The study of the inheritance of intelligence has been simplified by the introduction of intelligence tests. These were originally designed by the Frenchman Binet in 1911, to distinguish those children whose educational backwardness was mainly due to inherent lack of capacity from the children for whom other causes were more important. They have since been used extensively in the field of education, particularly in this country, for the selection of children for different types of secondary school at age eleven. Their value here has been that, with varied standards in our primary schools and with varied home backgrounds, intelligence tests at age eleven have been found to be more accurate than attainment tests at that age in predicting a child's performance in academic examinations at age sixteen. Such a test does not measure temperamental qualities important for success in school achievement, so most education authorities find it wise to use attainment tests and teachers' reports, as well as intelligence tests, in allocating children to secondary schools. Many, too, find it useful to give more than one test, since the kind of written intelligence test which can be given to groups of children is less reliable than are individual oral tests. Most of the tests involve special verbal ability as well as general ability and this may be no disadvantage in selecting children for most forms of academic education.

The particular value of the intelligence test for genetic study is that it makes it possible to grade children in the middle ranges of intelligence, though this grading cannot be so accurate as for a character, such as height, which can be directly measured. There are various ways of scoring tests. Perhaps the best is the percentile rating by which, for example, a child with a percentile rating of 67 would be one who scored better than 66 children out of 100 of the same age. A more usual way of scoring is to assign to the child a mental age, which is the age at which the average child makes the same score. An intelligence quotient is then derived by dividing the child's mental age by his real age and multiplying by 100. Thus a child with real age six years who scores as high as the average child of nine years would have an intelligence quotient (I.Q.) of 150; one who scored as low as the average child of three years would have an intelligence quotient of 50.

*Distribution of intelligence-test score*

Most intelligence tests, partly by design, give a distribution for intelligence quotients which is near that of a normal curve, at any rate down to a level of I.Q. 50. Below this level there are usually rather more children than will fit a normal curve, though this does not appear in the sample of Scottish children shown in Figure 43. The average is 100, by definition, on the group of children on which the test is standardized, but may differ in another group. The most commonly used individual intelligence test is the 1937 Terman Merrill revision of the Binet test. This was standardized in America and when administered to a really random group of 1,207 eleven-year-old children in Scotland in 1947 the average score was not 100, but 102·5 (104 for boys and 101 for girls). The standard deviation for the American series at age eleven was eighteen and for the Scottish series it was twenty. The distribution for the Scottish sample is shown in Figure 43.

The intelligence-test score expressed as either a percentile rating or an intelligence quotient is reasonably constant over the years seven to fifteen for the same test, provided that it is properly standardized at each age. A few children will show quite marked differences when tested on the same test after a short interval. A few children will show a fairly steady gain between the ages of seven and fifteen and a few will show a steady fall. Before the age of five and even more before the age of three intelligence quotients do not correspond closely with later results partly, perhaps, because testing is unreliable partly, perhaps, on the analogy of height, because genetic factors for intellectual development come into play gradually as the child matures. After the age of fifteen or sixteen the actual intelligence-test score does not rise, but remains fairly constant for many years. It has, however, a tendency to fall and the rate of fall varies, among other things, with occupation. After leaving school those

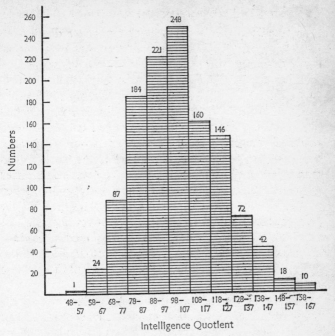

43. 1,207 Scottish eleven-year-old children, average I.Q. 102·5

who are engaged in manual work tend to lose their ability to score on intelligence tests fairly quickly; while those in non-manual occupations show little or no loss for a decade or even three decades; those going on to higher education may even improve their scores up to the age of twenty. A test at the age of fifteen predicts adult test scores fairly reliably. A test at the age of eleven has considerable predictive value as gains above and below the average level between eleven and fifteen will not greatly affect the total score.

*Intelligence-test score in twins*

The inheritance of intelligence-test score has been studied in several different ways, for example, in twins and families with adopted children. The twin studies of Newman, Freeman, and Holzinger were mentioned in Chapter 1. They found great resemblance between their fifty pairs of identical twins reared together. The fraternal twins were no more alike than non-twin brothers and sisters brought up in the same home. These findings are summarized in Table 6.

Table 6. A comparison of differences of I.Q. scores in MZ (identical) twins (reared together and apart) and DZ (fraternal) twins

| I.Q. differences | MZ twins reared together No.=50 | Like-sex DZ twins reared together No.=50 | Pairs of brothers and pairs of sisters No.=50 | MZ twins reared apart No.=19 | Same individuals tested a month later |
|---|---|---|---|---|---|
| 0–4 points | 24 | 16 | 20 | 7 | 26 |
| 5–9 points | 18 | 12 | 10 | 5 | 17 |
| 10–14 points | 7 | 12 | 6 | 3 | 6 |
| 15–19 points | 1 | 7 | 9 | 3 | 1 |
| 20–24 points | — | 2 | 2 | 1 | — |
| 25+ points | — | 1 | 3 | — | — |

The resemblance between the identical twins reared together is nearly as great as one would get on testing the same batch of fifty individuals twice at an interval of a month. The fraternal twins are no more alike than non-twin brothers and sisters. The identical twins reared apart are rather more alike than fraternal twins or brothers and sisters brought up in the same family.

A detailed study of these nineteen twins brought up apart is most interesting in illustrating the effect of social and educational differences on intelligence-test score. The findings of the Chicago survey are given in Table 7.

Table 7. A comparison of differences in I.Q. scores in identical twins reared apart (from Woodworth, after Newman, Freeman, and Holzinger)

| Case No. | Sex | Age at separation | Age when tested | ENVIRONMENTAL DIFFERENCES | | | I.Q. differences |
| | | | | In years of schooling | In estimated educational advantages | In estimated social advantages | |
| --- | --- | --- | --- | --- | --- | --- | --- |
| 11 | F | 18 months | 35 | 14 | 37 | 25 | 24 |
| 2 | F | 18 months | 27 | 15 | 32 | 14 | 12 |
| 18 | M | 1 year | 27 | 4 | 28 | 31 | 19 |
| 4 | F | 5 months | 29 | 4 | 22 | 15 | 17 |
| 12 | F | 18 months | 29 | 5 | 19 | 13 | 7 |
| 1 | F | 18 months | 19 | 1 | 15 | 27 | 12 |
| 17 | M | 2 years | 14 | 0 | 15 | 15 | 10 |
| 8 | F | 3 months | 15 | 1 | 14 | 32 | 15 |
| 3 | M | 2 months | 23 | 1 | 12 | 15 | −2 |
| 14 | F | 6 months | 39 | 0 | 12 | 15 | −1 |
| 5 | F | 14 months | 38 | 1 | 11 | 26 | 4 |
| 13 | M | 1 month | 19 | 0 | 11 | 13 | 1 |
| 10 | F | 1 year | 12 | 1 | 10 | 15 | 5 |
| 15 | M | 1 year | 26 | 2 | 9 | 7 | 1 |
| 7 | M | 1 month | 13 | 0 | 9 | 27 | 1 |
| 19 | F | 6 years | 41 | 0 | 9 | 14 | 9 |
| 16 | F | 2 years | 11 | 0 | 8 | 12 | 2 |
| 6 | F | 3 years | 59 | 0 | 7 | 10 | 8 |
| 9 | M | 1 month | 19 | 0 | 7 | 14 | 6 |

In this table an I.Q. difference is marked as negative when the difference is in the opposite direction to the educational advantage.

It will be seen from Table 7 that, superimposed on the general resemblances of identical twins reared apart, there are differences which can in most cases be related to differences in educational experience and, to a lesser degree, to a difference in estimated social advantage. It should be noted that, conveniently, a few of these American pairs had experienced greater difference in education than would be possible in Britain. In the pair at the top of the table, for example, one twin had a university degree, the other had had only three years of elementary education. Two English series of twins brought up apart, one including forty-two identical pairs collected at University College, London, and another thirty-eight pairs collected by an appeal on television and examined at the Maudsley Hospital, London, showed an even higher identical twin resemblance. In each case the correlation coefficient was about 0·8.

These twin studies show clearly that genetic factors are important in causing variation in intelligence-test score. But they also show that for intelligence-test score, much more, for example, than for height, environmental difference may be a cause of variation. This environmentally caused variation, however, will not, apart from trauma or disease affecting the brain, be more than about twenty points; while the normal variation which occurs in a population spans at least 100 points.

## Resemblance in intelligence-test scores within families

Because of these environmental effects, studies of the resemblances of relatives are not simple to interpret. In general, it seems that regressions towards the average of the population are much like those for height. The regression is about one half for brothers and sisters. For example, in 1940 Roberts found a regression of close to one half in a survey of all the ten-year-old children in Bath with their brothers and sisters of school age. Thus the average intelligence of the brothers of children with I.Q. 150 is about 125, and that for children with I.Q. 70 is about 85. It is perhaps surprising that the regression should be as much as half in view of the common

family environment of brothers and sisters and in view of
the fact that there is definite assortative marriage for intelligence.

The regression towards the average of son's intelligence
from father's or mother's intelligence is less well established,
partly because of the unreliability of testing adult intelligence.
However, a comparison of children's intelligence with that
of their father's occupation, again suggests a regression of
half. The average I.Q. of men in the major professions in
this country is of the order of 135 on the Terman Merrill test.
For example, in the 1947 Scottish survey a group test was
given to 88 per cent of the eleven-year-old children, about
7,100 in all, and a Terman Merrill test to a random sample
of 1,207. There were 143 children of men in the major professions taking the group test and their average score was
54·3, which corresponds approximately to a Terman Merrill
I.Q. of 122. Since the average intelligence of the boys taking
the test was 104, this gives a regression to the mean of about
0·4. In contrast, the average intelligence score of the sons of
unskilled workers was 31·1, corresponding approximately
to a Terman Merrill I.Q. of 94; the average I.Q. of men in
unskilled occupations is about 90. A more direct estimate of
the regression from intelligent fathers is given by Terman's
study of gifted children in California. He collected a group
of children with I.Q.s over 135 and an average I.Q. of 152.
In 1945 these children had grown up and it was possible to
test 400 of their offspring. The average score of the offspring
was 128, giving a regression towards the mean of a little
less than half, if the American average is taken as 100. As
with brothers, it is surprising that sons should regress nearly
half-way in view of the similar environment of father and son
and of assortative marriage.

It has already been explained when discussing height that
the tendency for regresssion towards the mean of the population to occur from father or mother to son does not imply

that the amount of variation from one generation to another will decrease. Neglecting environmental factors it will be exceptional for a man of average intelligence to have a very intelligent son. But since there are a great number of average and near-average men their exceptionally intelligent children will form a substantial proportion of the intelligent men and women of the next generation. Regression to the mean is part of the reason for the finding that about a third of the sons of professional men do not reach a sufficiently high intelligence-test score for admission to a grammar school and about half do not themselves enter a profession or occupation of similar social status. It is also part of the reason for the finding that about half the children selected for grammar-school education are sons of skilled manual workers. An additional reason, however, for this social mobility is that occupation is only a rough guide to intelligence.

## Intelligence-test score in adopted children

In an attempt to get over the difficulty that much of the resemblance between near relatives may be due to common family environment, a number of psychologists have attempted studies of adopted or foster children. They have related the test scores of the adopted children to the occupations of their adopting parents and, where possible, their natural parents. A difficulty here is the tendency of some adoption societies to try and match natural and adopting parents by placing the child of a middle-class mother in a middle-class adoptive home, and that of a working-class mother in a working-class adoptive home. In general, these studies of adopted children are agreed in showing a relation between the adopted child's test score and the occupation of the adopting father or the educational level of the adopting mother. This will be due to environment or selective placing. These studies show, however, that this relationship is much less close than that between a father or mother and their own natural children, even when the adopted children were adopted in infancy. The findings of one such American study by Leahy are reproduced in Table 8. In this study all the children were placed in their foster homes before the age of six months and were tested between the age of five and fourteen. There was thought to be relatively little selective placement.

Table 8. A comparison between father's occupation and intelligence-test score of natural and adopted children

| FATHER'S OCCUPATION | ADOPTED CHILDREN | | OWN CHILDREN | |
|---|---|---|---|---|
| | No. | average score | No. | average score |
| Professional | 43 | 112·6 | 40 | 118·6 |
| Managerial | 38 | 111·6 | 42 | 117·6 |
| Clerical and skilled manual | 44 | 110·6 | 43 | 106·9 |
| Semi-skilled | 45 | 109·4 | 46 | 101·1 |
| Unskilled | 24 | 107·8 | 23 | 102·1 |

Among the adopted children, with probably only environmental differences at work, the range of intelligence by father's occupation is a little less than five points. In the natural children, where genetic as well as environmental influences are operating, the range is over seventeen points, more than three times as much. The natural children of professional men are, on the average, significantly more intelligent than their adopted brothers, while the natural children of unskilled workers are significantly less intelligent than are their adopted brothers. The possible importance of environmental influences before birth should not be forgotten, but there is no reason at the moment to attribute much importance to them in relation to intelligence. The high average intelligence of both groups of children in this study is striking and probably reflects the skill of the agencies arranging adoptions in choosing parents who provide a good environment for children.

The studies of the intelligence-test scores of adopted children in relation to the intelligence of their true mothers lead to much the same conclusions. One of the most interesting of these was a study in America by Skodak and Skeels in which the educational status and the intelligence-test score of the true biological mothers were available. The children were placed in the adopting homes at the average age of three months with apparently little selective placement. They were tested on four occasions over a span of ten to thirteen years. The educational status but not the intelligence of the adopting parents was known. As with other studies, there was a small positive relationship between the child's score and the occupation and education of the adopting parents.

This relationship did not increase as the child grew older. On the other hand the order of the children's scores became increasingly related to that of the natural mother's test score as the children grew older, although they had had no contact with their natural mothers since early infancy. This increasing resemblance may reasonably be attributed to the increasing influence of genetic factors on intellectual development as the child grows. The final correlation between the children's order of intelligence and that of their natural mothers was 0·4, which is nearly as much as one finds between true mothers and the children they have brought up themselves. The relations are shown in Figure 44.

A second important finding in this American study, this time showing environmental influence on intelligence-test score, was that, although the order in which the children were placed by the test was related to that in which their mothers were placed by the same test, the children's scores as a whole were lifted well above that of their mothers. The mothers, who had mostly grown up in unfortunate circumstances, had an average I.Q. of 86. One might have expected therefore

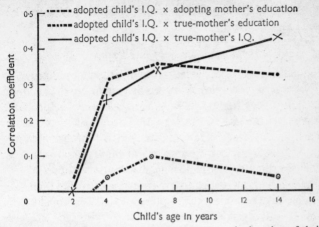

44. Adopted children's I.Q. related to the I.Q. and education of their natural mothers and the education of their adopting mothers (after Honzik from Skodak and Skeels)

that, even allowing for environmental depression of the mother's scores, the children's genetic component for intelligence would be a little below average. In fact their average score was well above average, 112 at age six and still above average, namely 106, at age thirteen. Allowing for some environmental depression of the mothers' scores, it would seem likely that the children's scores had been lifted by the good homes provided by the adopting parents some ten points above the level one would have expected from the ordinary regression of child's score on one parent's score.

Summing up, one may say that the evidence from twin studies and from studies of adopted children suggests that much of the variation in general intelligence among school children as measured by intelligence-test score is due to variation in genetic endowment, but that an appreciable amount is also due to variation in educational experience and home background. Probably more than half the variation in Britain today is genetic, and this proportion will increase as educational opportunity and the standard of living become more uniform.

## Mechanism of the inheritance of intelligence

The mechanism of the inheritance of general intelligence, in view of the part played by environment in determining intelligence, will not be easy to unravel. It is probable that numerous genetic factors are concerned in much the same way as for height, and, in fact, most of the resemblances found between relatives are close to those which would be given by simple multifactorial inheritance, without dominance and without assortative marriage. Even more than with height, however, this nice agreement with theory must be due to the mutually balancing effects of modifying factors, genetic and environmental. On the genetic side, as with height, assortative marriage will tend to lessen the tendency of relatives to regress towards the mean of the population, while dominance will tend to increase it. On the environmental side, common family background will also tend to increase the resemblance between relatives; but damage to the brain during intrauterine development or at birth, which, in major degree, causes severe mental deficiency may, in minor degree, lessen the resemblance between relatives. In addition there is a greater margin of error in measuring intelligence than, for example, in measuring height and this will tend to lessen the resemblance between relatives for intelligence-test score.

## Inheritance of special abilities

Not much is known about the inheritance of special abilities, partly because tests to measure these abilities are not yet fully developed. There are individual families in which special talents have occurred more frequently than could be due to chance and at a level of distinction which could hardly just be due to family influence and example. For instance, the mathematicians in the Bernouilli family, the musicians

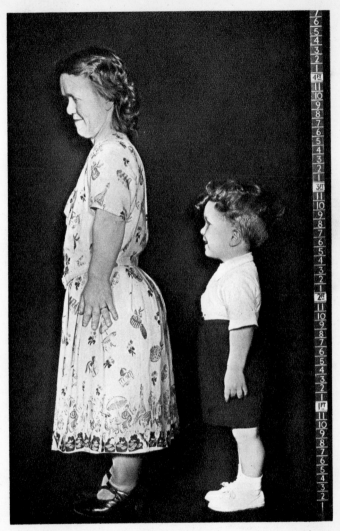

Achondroplasia in mother (height 4 ft 3 ins.) and five-year-old son (height 3 ft). Height of average English woman is 5 ft 4 ins., and average five-year-old boy 3 ft 6 ins.

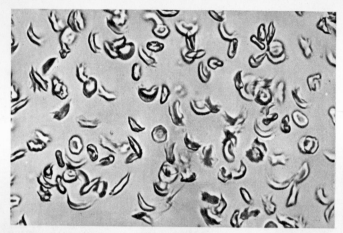

(a) Sickling of red blood cells in a child with severe anaemia and homozygous for the gene for sickle-cell haemoglobin

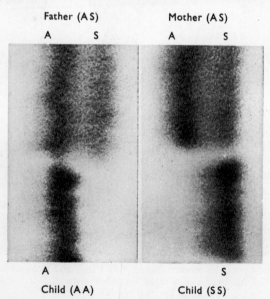

Father (AS)                    Mother (AS)

A        S                    A        S

A                              S

Child (AA)                    Child (SS)

(b) Electrical separation of haemoglobins A and S in the family of a child with severe sickle-cell anaemia

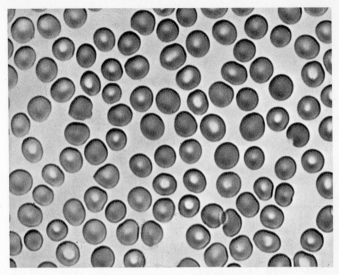

(a) Normal red blood cells. Magnification × 600

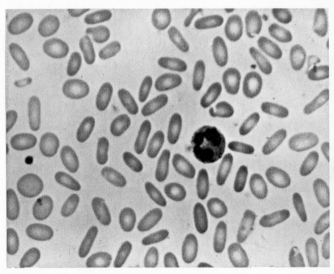

(b) Oval red blood cells. Magnification × 600

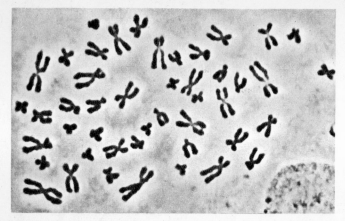

(a) Chromosomes in a normal male. Magnification × 2,160

(b) Chromosomes arranged in pairs and numbered; the X and Y chromosomes are shown separately. Magnification × 1,800

in the Bach family, and, in Britain, the scientists in the Darwin family. Britain's highest distinction for scientists is Fellowship of the Royal Society and each of the four generations of the direct male descendants of Erasmus Darwin, himself a Fellow, has contained one or more Fellows. The sciences of evolution and genetics owe much to this English country doctor, as Charles Darwin was one of his grandsons and Francis Galton another. But caution is needed in drawing conclusions from individual pedigrees, such as those in Figures 45 and 46. Quantitative methods are needed for analysing and measuring special abilities before their inheritance can be effectively studied. In part, such pedigrees are due to the inheritance of general intelligence and the influence of the home.

## Inheritance of characteristics of personality

The same difficulty in measuring holds, at present, for the inheritance of facets of personality other than intelligence. Eysenck has put forward evidence for a dimension of personality ranging from marked introversion on the one hand to marked extraversion on the other; a twin study has indicated much greater resemblance for identical than fraternal twins in scores on this dimension and so indicated some degree of genetic determination. Similarly, Eysenck has presented twin evidence that genetic factors are important for another dimension of personality which corresponds to neuroticism.

One should perhaps be especially cautious in attributing similarity in personality in identical twins reared together, to their identical genetic constitution. The similarity of their habits and interests may be a strong environmental source of resemblance in personality characteristics. It is interesting, therefore, that the preliminary report on the thirty-eight British twins reared apart, usually from birth, collected by a television appeal, shows a definite resemblance for assess-

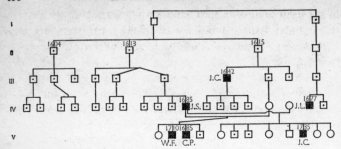

■ = notable composers – Johann Christoph (III₇); the great Johann
Sebastian (IV₁₁); Johann Ludwig (IV₁₈); Wilhelm Friedemann (V₂);
Carl Philipp (V₃); Johann Christian, English Bach,(V₁₀)

▣ = musicians – In generation IV these included the cathedral
organists at Eisenach (IV₃), Arnstadt (IV₆), Keula (IV₇),
Ohrduf (IV₈), Jena (IV₁₂), Mulhausen (IV₁₇), Meiningen (IV₁₉)

### 45. Part of the pedigree of the Bach family of Thuringia (Germany)

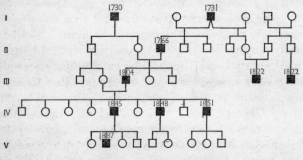

■ = Fellow of the Royal Society

I₁ Josiah Wedgwood, potter; I₃ Erasmus Darwin, physician
II₃ Robert Darwin, physician
III₃ Charles Darwin, biologist; III₆ Francis Galton, geneticist;
III₇ Douglas Galton, engineer
IV₅ George Darwin, astronomer; IV₇ Francis Darwin, botanist;
IV₉ Horace Darwin, scientific-instrument maker
V₂ Charles Darwin, physicist

### 46. Part of the pedigree of the Darwin family

ments both of introversion-extraversion and neuroticism for the identical pairs, though the resemblance is less than the high degree of resemblance found for intelligence-test score in this group.

## Selection and intelligence – the past

Taking the view over hundreds of thousands of years, it is obvious that in the evolution of man there has been a steady selection for intelligence. The two main indications are an increase in brain size, shown by the internal cubic capacity of fossil skulls, and the improvements in techniques of making tools and weapons. The relationship between brain size and intelligence is not close, but there is a relationship. The relationship between culture and intelligence is also, perhaps, not very close, because even under primitive conditions one group of men could learn techniques from another and perhaps improve on them, without necessarily being more intelligent. But, taking both brain size and culture together it seems likely that the intelligence of man's ancestors improved steadily between the times of the earliest Australopithecine ape-men, perhaps 2,000,000 years ago, and the earliest men who were undoubtedly of our own species appearing in the second half of the fourth and last Ice Age about 25,00 years ago.

The average brain size of modern men and women is about 1,400 cubic centimetres (i.e. $2\frac{1}{2}$ pints). The Australopithecines had a brain size, on the average, of only about 600 cubic centimetres (i.e. 1 pint), of much the same order as that of present-day gorillas. Unlike gorillas, however, it is now certain that some of the Australopithecines were tool-makers and were responsible for the simple contemporary manufactured stone tools to be found in South Aftica. The Java and Pekin ape-men, *Homo erectus* of about 250,000 years ago mostly had brain sizes of the order of 900 to 1,300 cubic centimetres. The Neanderthaloids, who were dominant in Europe and Asia at the end of the third inter-glacial and the first half of the fourth Ice Age up to about 50,000 years ago, had brains of modern size. The men of our own species who replaced them, perhaps with some admixture, also had brains of full modern size.

There are, therefore, no anatomical indications of any increase in intelligence since the middle of the last Ice Age and even on the cultural side these ancient Europeans were as advanced as several primitive peoples of the present time. On the cultural side it is very difficult to relate achievement to intelligence over this period. It is clear that the men and women in the Near East from about 9,000 to 6,000 years ago who made the Neolithic revolution must have included some individuals of great natural ability. They invented all the main elements of our present-day culture, agriculture, stock-keeping, building in stone, weaving, pottery, and writing. Throughout the historical period, written records show that in certain times and places there have been men and women who, perhaps in particularly favourable circumstances, have been able to show intelligence comparable with anything found today. This is most clearly seen in fields such as art, religion, and philosophy which depend most on the creative thought of each individual rather than the assimilation of earlier advances. The education of some of the brightest of present-day undergraduates can usefully be based on the writings of poets and philosophers of ancient civilizations. There are, then, no clear indications of a rise in average intelligence in historical times.

One might have expected intelligence to have continued selective advantages in man and this apparent lack of advance in intelligence for many thousands of years is perhaps surprising. One suggestion to account for it is that brain size at birth is limited by the size of outlet of the mother's pelvis through which the baby's head must pass. One would have expected, however, that the size of the pelvis in women would be capable of responding further to selective forces by further increase in size. A second suggestion is that selection for intelligence has been intense in the past and a plateau has been reached which makes full use of the available genetic variation. In that case, appreciable further advance would depend on the slow accumulation of new variation from gene mutation. The situation would be similar to that which now holds for milk yield in some of the best herds of dairy cows and for egg production in some of the best flocks of poultry. But there is still a great deal of genetic variation for intelligence in all populations and, if this latter theory were correct, one might expect the average man and woman to be much nearer the level of the cleverest.

A third and important suggestion is that the situation for intelligence is much the same as that which we have suggested applies for height. That is to say, that the man or woman of average intelligence is intrinsically biologically fitter and has more surviving children than either the dull or the clever. One way that the bright might be less fit is that cleverness might be associated with poor physical health. It is, in fact, a widely-held popular belief that clever children tend to be inferior in health and strength to the average child. But studies on this point have shown that this is not the case and that clever children are, in general, healthier and stronger than the average.

Another way that the clever might be less biologically fit is that they might tend to be physiologically infertile. There is little general evidence on the relation of infecundity, that is physiological infertility, to intelligence. Galton noted that where there is inheritance of property, one way of rising in the social scale, alternative to having ability, is to be a member of an infertile family and inherit money. He drew attention to the number of English families that came to an end in the direct male line, through marriage to heiresses. The reason he suggested was that these heiresses are only heiresses because they have no brothers or sisters with whom to share their parents' property. It is doubtful if processes of this kind have occurred to a sufficient degree to produce a real genetic association between ability and infecundity. It is much more likely that any association of intelligence with infertility is due to the ability of intelligent people to plan the size of their families rather than leave this to nature.

## Current trends – differential fertility by social class

Since reliable statistics became available about a hundred years ago, it has been noted in Britain and other countries with a similar culture that there is a striking relationship between social class and family size. For most of this period the relationship was inverse and consistent; the lower a man's social class the greater, on the average, was his fertility. Although the different occupational classes include men of a wide range of intellectual ability, there is, in general, a direct relationship between occupation and intelligence as measured. It is probable that part of this relationship is with genetic endowment for intelligence. The inverse relationship of average family size with class suggests, therefore, a tendency for the more intelligent men to have fewest children. This inverse relationship was already present in the 1850s. It became more marked in the second half of the century and has, until recently, remained fairly constant in spite of the fall in the birth-rate of all classes. Estimates from the Family Census of 1946 of the average size of completed families of non-manual and manual workers in Great Britain for three periods are shown in Table 9.

The figures take no account of the differences in the proportion of men in each group who are married, but this would not greatly alter the fertility ratio. The changes in total fertility in each occupational group must be due to the spread of the practice of family planning; they are much too rapid to be due to changes in genetically determined fecundity.

Table 9. Secular change in family size by social class

| Date of marriage | Family size | | Ratio of manual to non-manual |
|---|---|---|---|
| | Non-manual workers | Manual workers | |
| 1900–9 | 2·79 | 3·94 | 1·41 |
| 1915–19 | 2·05 | 2·91 | 1·42 |
| 1925–9 | 1·73 | 2·49 | 1·44 |

The non-manual workers in 1900–9 were having more children than manual workers were having in 1925–9. At the present time, therefore, any tendency for genes determining intellectual brightness to be associated with genes determining family size will be with genes affecting the psychological and social determinants of family size, rather than genes controlling fecundity. It is difficult to say just how far back into the history of Britain beyond 1850 this tendency of the upper social classes to plan small families goes and to what extent it was accompanied by a similar tendency for the more intelligent within each social class to plan their families. Obviously, however, since intelligent individuals tend to rise in the social scale, fertility differences between social classes might counteract any tendency of natural selection to favour intelligent individuals.

It is interesting to note, however, that in recent years the relationship between occupational class and family size appears to be changing. In the 1951 Census of England and Wales the figures for more recent marriages suggested that, within the non-manual groups, the wives of men in the more intellectually and educationally demanding occupations were having larger families. Within the manual groups however, the old relationship persisted. A similar change was noted in Germany and Scandinavia even before the Second World War and in America since the war.

The new trend can be seen more clearly for England and Wales in the recently reported fertility figures for the ten per

cent sample in the 1961 census. The ratio of family size in
manual workers compared with non-manual workers has
fallen to 1·27 for marriages of twenty-five to twenty-nine
years duration (completed families), and to 1·16 for mar-

Table 10. Average family size of women married once only
and enumerated with their husbands by husbands' socio-economic
group (agriculture, armed forces, 'indefinite', and a few others
excluded) England and Wales 1961. Ten per cent sample.

| Socio-economic group | Approximate percentage in group | Family size marriage duration 15–19 years | Change (per cent relative to marriage duration 25–29 years |
|---|---|---|---|
| Professional – self employed | 0·89 | 2·18 | +17 |
| Professional – employed | 2·92 | 1·90 | +13 |
| Employers and managers – large units | 4·55 | 1·85 | +10 |
| Employers and managers – small units | 6·98 | 1·83 | +3 |
| Intermediate non-manual | 4·20 | 1·80 | +8 |
| Junior non-manual | 12·21 | 1·76 | +5 |
| Self-employed – not professional | 3·93 | 1·92 | +7 |
| Foremen and supervisors – manual | 4·27 | 1·99 | +2 |
| Skilled manual workers | 30·56 | 2·11 | 0 |
| Semi-skilled manual workers | 14·72 | 2·15 | –2 |
| Unskilled manual workers | 6·88 | 2·34 | –5 |

riages of fifteen to nineteen years duration (where families
will be more than nine-tenths complete). Family size by the
main occupational groups (excluding those in agriculture),
in roughly descending order of average intellectual requirement of the occupation, are shown in Table 10 for marriages
of fifteen to nineteen years duration and also the percentage
change in relation to marriages of twenty-five to twenty-nine
years duration.

The differences in fertility between farmers and farm workers are small and their fertility is relatively high. In the
non-manual occupational groups the relationship between intellectual requirement and fertility is consistent and positive,
a fall from 2·18 for self-employed professional to 1·76 for
junior non-manual. In the manual groups the relationship is
also consistent, but is negative – a rise from 1·99 for foremen
to 2·34 for unskilled manual workers. Comparing the family
size of marriages of fifteen to nineteen years with those of
twenty-five to twenty-nine years duration the overall difference between non-manual and manual has lessened, the
direct relationship between family size and intellectual

Table 11. White women aged thirty-five to thirty-nine married
once and husband present; urban areas of U.S.A. 1950
Census, 3.3 per cent sample

|  | No. in thousands | Average size of family | Per cent change since 1940 | Distribution by family size | | | | | |
|---|---|---|---|---|---|---|---|---|---|
|  |  |  |  | 0 | 1 | 2 | 3 | 4 | 5+ |
| Professional | 256 | 1·79 | +11·9 | 18·0 | 22·4 | 35·2 | 16·6 | 5·0 | 2·9 |
| Proprietors | 426 | 1·90 | + 7·8 | 18·7 | 22·5 | 35·3 | 16·6 | 6·2 | 3·6 |
| Clerical | 356 | 1·76 | + 7·0 | 20·1 | 24·6 | 31·4 | 14·2 | 5·8 | 3·9 |
| Craftsmen | 550 | 2·06 | − 5·2 | 15·9 | 23·4 | 30·2 | 16·8 | 7·9 | 6·8 |
| Operatives | 107 | 2·16 | − 6·0 | 16·8 | 20·9 | 28·3 | 16·9 | 8·5 | 8·6 |
| Labourers | 98 | 2·51 | − 5·6 | 15·1 | 19·0 | 26·4 | 14·9 | 10·3 | 14·3 |

requirement in the non-manual groups has increased, and the reverse relationship in the manual groups has decreased; though future births may somewhat modify the latter trend.

The most likely explanation of these changes is that there is a progressive tendency for the more intelligent parents to plan larger families, and that this is being revealed as the practice of family planning spreads down through the socio-economic groups.

Similar trends have been noted in American national statistics where the differences in fertility by occupational class and even more by educational status have lessened appreciably between the censuses of 1940 and 1950. Table 11 shows, for the urban areas of America, the average family size for white women aged between thirty-five and thirty-nine in 1950 by the occupations of their husbands, together with the percentage change in the average family size since 1940 and the percentage with families of each size.

The differences in fertility within marriage are still considerable in 1950, but are much less than those of 1940. Looking to the future, it is to be expected that the number of large

Table 12. Ever-married white women aged thirty-five to thirty-nine: urban areas of U.S.A. 1950 Census, 3.3 per cent sample

| Wife's education Type and length in years | No. in thousands | Average size of family | Per cent change since 1940 | Distribution of family by size | | | | |
|---|---|---|---|---|---|---|---|---|
| | | | | 0 | 1 | 2 | 3 | 4+ |
| College 4 or more | 186 | 1·69 | +22·6 | 21·5 | 22·8 | 33·3 | 15·4 | 7·0 |
| College 1–3 | 288 | 1·72 | + 9·4 | 21·4 | 22·5 | 31·7 | 15·2 | 8·2 |
| High School 4 | 966 | 1·71 | + 5·7 | 21·4 | 25·5 | 30·3 | 13·7 | 9·2 |
| High School 1–3 | 720 | 1·98 | — 2·4 | 18·1 | 23·6 | 28·7 | 15·4 | 14·3 |
| None or Elementary | 898 | 2·31 | — 7·7 | 16·8 | 20·2 | 25·9 | 19·1 | 19·9 |

unplanned families in the manual working groups will fall steadily, and that ultimate differences in fertility by occupation will depend mostly on the relative proportion of two-, three-, and four-child families in each group.

The census data on the fertility of married women according to the amount and type of education they have received are given in Table 12.

Similar trends again are seen in the French 1954 Census, in which at ten years marriage duration, the professional class had larger families than any other non-manual occupational class.

*Children's test scores in relation to their family size*

Several studies have been made, both in Britain and the United States, relating a child's intelligence-test score to the number of his brothers and sisters. The largest-scale investigation which collected information of this kind was the Scottish Mental Survey of 1947, but similar results have been obtained in smaller-scale English and American surveys. The finding of the Scottish Survey was that the more brothers and sisters a child had, the lower, on the average, was his test score. This shows up on the whole sample, given a group intelligence test, and also on the sample of 1,207 children given the more accurate individual Terman Merrill test. The relation between number of brothers and sisters and

Table 13. Relationship between the number of a child's brothers and sisters and his Terman Merrill I.Q. Scottish Survey, 1947

|  | *Number of brothers and sisters* | | | | | | | |
|---|---|---|---|---|---|---|---|---|
|  | 0 | 1 | 2 | 3 | 4 | 5 | 6 | 7+ |
| *Average I.Q.* | 110 | 109 | 106 | 101 | 96 | 92 | 96 | 91 |
| *No. of Survey children* | 144 | 279 | 227 | 194 | 101 | 94 | 65 | 96 |

Terman Merrill I.Q. can be made for completed families since the inquiry was made again when the eleven-year-old children had reached the age of eighteen. The relationship is shown in Table 13.

Children's intelligence is in part an indication of that of their parents, so these findings suggest, like the findings of fertility in relation to occupational class, that the duller parents have the most children. Further, this would appear to be true within each occupational class. Two possible objections to this conclusion are: firstly, that a survey through children takes no account of men and women who have no children at all; secondly, that the mere fact of being a member of a large family tends to depress the environmental component of intelligence-test score. Both objections are in part valid. The effect of being a member of a large family appears to apply most strongly to the verbal element in intelligence tests. The reason suggested for this is that the smaller the family the more the child speaks to and is spoken to by his parents. The exclusion of the unmarried and the childless may also be important, since, though there are no great differences in marriage rates between socio-economic groups, it may be the less intelligent in each group who tend to remain single.

*A comparison of children's intelligence in a large population after an interval of fifteen years.*

Only one large scale direct measurement in the intelligence level of school children has been made. The Scottish Survey of all school children aged eleven years in 1947 may be compared with a similar survey of all children in 1932. This shows a very small gain in average intelligence-test score over the fifteen years. The gain is perhaps less than one would have anticipated if genetic factors had remained constant, in view of the improvements in environment over this period and the reduction in average family size. These environmental improvements have been sufficient to raise

average height in eleven-year-old school children by more
than an inch and weight by several pounds. The negligible
rise in intelligence-test score suggests that environmental gain
has been offset by a fall in the average genetic component
for intelligence, but there are other possible interpretations.

### A direct study of fertility related to intelligence-test score

The most valuable clue to any selection now occurring for
intelligence will come from a direct comparison of the number of children born to men and women whose families are
complete and whose intelligence-test score was estimated
when they were between the ages of fifteen and twenty. The
first figures will probably come from Sweden. National Service was introduced there in 1944 and the recruits, aged
twenty, are given an intelligence test. The recruits from
southern Sweden born in 1924 and called for service in 1944
are now being followed by Quensel at the Institute of
Statistics in Lund. The marriage rate and family size by
1953, when the men were twenty-nine, is already known.
Many of these men are only just starting their families, but
the findings are already of interest. The intelligence-test
scores are given as actual scores and not quotients, the average score on the test being about seventy.

The first interesting finding is that the proportion who are
married by 1953 increases steadily as the intelligence score
increases, except at the highest levels of intelligence. At this
very high level it is natural that marriage should be post-
poned since many of these men are still training for their
professions well after the age of twenty. The proportion
married rises from only two-fifths for those scoring 0–9, to
two-thirds for those making an average score of about 70,
to nearly three-quarters for those scoring 110–119, falling
off to about two-thirds again for the really high scorers.
There is good reason to suppose that the high scorers will
catch up. It is known from earlier studies that Swedish

students who complete a secondary education and matriculate do not catch up the average of the population in the proportion married till their early thirties but, ultimately, 90 per cent of them marry, compared with only about 85 per cent of the general population.

To illustrate the way the families are developing, Quensel put the men into four broad groups. A dull group of 1,135 men scoring 0–49, an average group of 2,077 scoring 50–99, and two bright groups, one of 470 scoring 100 or over but only educated at primary schools, and the other of 356 who had at least secondary school education. A large majority of the latter group also scored 100 or over.

The status of the families in 1953 when the men were twenty-nine is shown in Table 14 which gives the percentage married and the percentage with at least one, two, and three children. It will be seen that column 1(b) refers to children born before marriage and that these mark an important contribution, over one-seventh, to the fertility of the group of low intelligence and over one-ninth in the case of the average group:

Table 14. Marriage rates and fertility of twenty-nine-year-old Swedes by intelligence-test score. Recruits born 1924

| Score | Number | Per cent married | Per cent with 1, 2, and 3 children | | | | Total children per 100 men |
|-------|--------|------------------|------|------|------|------|-----------------------------|
|       |        |                  | 1(b) | 1(a) | 2    | 3    |                             |
| 0–49      | 1,135 | 57·1 | 9·8 | 31·7 | 19·7 | 4·7 | 65·9 |
| 59–99     | 2,077 | 68·0 | 8·3 | 38·9 | 22·2 | 5·2 | 74·6 |
| 100+      | 470   | 71·9 | 3·4 | 44·9 | 17·7 | 3·0 | 69·0 |
| Secondary | 356   | 66·0 | 1·7 | 43·3 | 17·4 | 0·3 | 62·7 |

1(b) – born before marriage.
1(a) – born after marriage.

The way in which these families have been built up since the men were twenty-three in 1947 is shown in Figure 47. In this

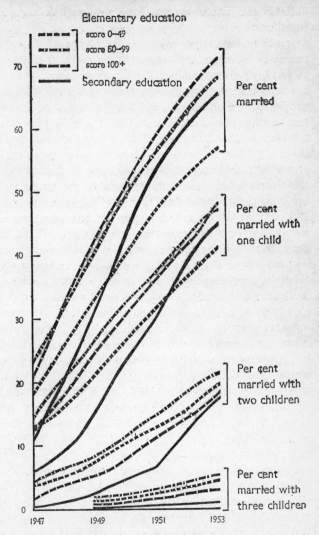

47. The marriage rates and fertility of twenty-nine-year-old Swedes
by intelligence test score. Recruits born 1924

diagram the first born, pre- and post-marital, are added
together.

It will be seen from Table 14 and Figure 47 that at age
twenty-nine the average group, scoring 50–99, have the highest fertility per man, married and single combined. They have
the second highest proportion married, the second highest
proportion with one child, and the highest proportion with
two and three children. The dull group, scoring 0–49, have
the highest fertility within marriage, but the lowest proportion married. Their total fertility is surpassed by all but the
group with secondary education, and they would not surpass
this group but for the children born before marriage and
made legitimate by the marriage. The bright group, scoring
100 or over, who had only a primary education have the
highest proportion married, the highest proportion with one
child, in spite of having relatively few pre-marital children
and the second highest total fertility. The remainder of the
bright group, those with at least a secondary education,
understandably tend to marry later and their total fertility is,
at twenty-nine, still the lowest. This group is, however,
showing the most rapid rise in family building at the time
when the survey finished, and separate studies of Swedish
matriculants show that they are now achieving a fertility
above the national average.

There can be no certain prediction of the future fertility
of the four groups. Quensel suggests that the fertility within
marriage of the dull group is likely to remain high, as they
will have difficulty in practising birth control. On the other
hand, the proportion of this dull group who marry will probably remain low in comparison with the other groups. The
bright group with only a primary education show promise
of passing the average group in fertility, as do the highly
educated group. When the groups are restudied after their
fertility is complete it will be no surprise if it is found that
they show a tendency for fertility to be positively related to

intelligence-test score. This will not necessarily mean that there is selection for the genetic factors favouring high intelligence in the population of Sweden. It is just possible that the whole relationship will be due to some environmental factors which depress both a man's score and the number of children he has; but this is unlikely.

Two recent studies from the U.S.A., from Minneapolis and Kalamazoo County, of completed families have shown the same trends. The very bright had the highest fertility, then came the dull, and the lowest fertility was in the group of average intelligence. In both studies there was, overall, a small positive relationship between intelligence and fertility, though selection might be neutral if allowance was made for length of generation.

A working hypothesis is that there have been three phases in selection for intelligence in west European countries and North America.

In phase one there was little family limitation, except in the highest social groups, and fertility was high and balanced by high infant and child mortality. In this phase there was probably some positive natural selection for intelligence since, on the whole, the more intelligent parents managed to rear more of their children.

In phase two, now current, infant mortality is much reduced and the practice of family planning spreading through the population becomes more important in determining selection than success in child rearing. In this phase there is some selection against intelligence, since the more intelligent parents tend to practise family limitation and plan the size of their families, while the duller parents tend still to have natural families.

In phase three, into which it is to be hoped that our civilization is now passing, nearly all families are planned. In this phase there is once more positive selection for intelligence since the more intelligent men and women tend to have the higher marriage rates and plan the larger families.

*Intellectual differences between races of man*

It is almost inevitable that selective forces for intelligence should have differed in different parts of the world. Accordingly, there will very probably be differences in the distribution of genes concerned with the development of general intelligence and special abilities in different races of man, just as there are differences in the distribution of the genes for blood groups and for other physical characters. This is a difficult problem, however, to examine objectively because of the environmental component in intelligence-test score. While this environmental element is probably less important than the genetic in comparing children who have had as uniform an environment as children in Britain today, it becomes of major importance in comparing, for example, French children with native African children of a tribe untouched by civilization. It is generally agreed that the search for a 'culture-free' intelligence test has failed.

The experience of universities in this country and in France is that students of first-rate ability come from India, China, and Vietnam, but less often from among natives of Africa south of the Sahara. Similarly, the small Chinese population in the United States is already making an impressive contribution to science and medicine and includes two recent Nobel Prize winners in theoretical physics. The contribution to scientific research of the much larger population in America of African descent would seem to be less. The cultural background is, however, very different. The Indians, the Vietnamese, and the Chinese have a long tradition of advanced civilization behind them, whereas the African Negro, in general, has not.

It is clear, however, that any differences that there may be in average intellectual ability of different races are small compared with the variation that occurs within each race. Every race that has so far been investigated has been found to include both highly intelligent and very backward individuals.

## CHAPTER 8

# Gene Mutations: their Frequency and Effects

IN the ordinary way genes are transmitted from generation to generation essentially unchanged. Their effects are modified by environment and by interaction with other genes with which they find themselves, but the gene itself transmitted to each generation is almost always faithfully copied. In the early 1900s the Dutch botanist, De Vries, one of the rediscoverers of Mendel's law, suggested that the sudden sports that appeared in flowers and were then genetically transmitted were essentially due to a change in a gene. He gave the name 'mutation' to this process.

Mutations can conveniently, if somewhat artificially, be divided into two groups according to the amount of chromosome involved. Those in which a single gene-locus is involved are called gene or point mutations. Those in which a section of a chromosome, involving perhaps numerous gene-loci, is affected are called chromosome mutations. The study of chromosome mutations in man is making rapid progress and will be considered separately in Chapter 10.

### Rate at which gene mutations occur

It has been found in animals such as the fruitfly that each gene locus has its own characteristic mutation rate. The mutation rate per gene-locus per generation may be defined as the reciprocal of the average number of generations that elapse before a mutation occurs at that particular gene-locus. Alternatively, the mutation rate will be given by the proportion of germ cells containing a fresh mutation at that gene-locus. A mutation that will occur, on the average, once in 50,000 generations at one gene-locus, will be newly present

155

in one out of 50,000 sperm or egg cells. Most naturally occurring mutation rates that have been measured in animals are between one in 10,000 and one in 100,000.

It is supposed that the majority of gene mutations occur in the process of formation of germ cells, so that normally only one of a parent's germ cells will contain the mutation. It is possible that mutations might occur during the formation of the sex glands themselves so that a section of the whole gland contains the mutation. This section would produce numerous germ cells containing the mutation. But experience suggests that this is a relatively rare occurrence.

The mutations that can occur at a particular gene-locus seem to be limited. The same mutations are constantly occurring and have occurred repeatedly in the past. The mutant gene can mutate back to the original form of the gene and also it can mutate further to give yet another alternative form of the gene. But neither of these processes will be of practical importance unless the mutant form of the gene becomes fairly common.

## Causes of gene mutation

The essential nature of most gene mutations is probably that there is a failure in the copying process at that particular part of the chromosome as it grows before cell division. The causes are mostly unknown. It is possible to increase mutation rate in animals by various influences applied to the sex glands, by ionizing radiation, by ultra-violet light, and by certain chemicals. The only one of these influences known to be important naturally is ionizing radiation. The chemicals concerned are not normally present in the body and ultra-violet light does not penetrate below the skin in man. Judging from animal experiments, however, the ionizing radiation that man experiences accounts for only a small fraction of all mutation, and agents as yet unknown must be responsible for the rest.

In the course of the thirty years from birth to the average age of conceiving children, most men and women receive about three units of ionizing radiation to their sex glands from natural sources. This is made up of cosmic rays, rays from radioactive rocks in the earth, and radiation from radioactive chemicals in the individuals' own blood-streams. The dose of radiation needed experimentally to double the mutation rate in male mice appears to be sixty units when the radiation is given quickly, which is nearly twenty times the naturally-occurring radiation. The doubling dose may be greater still if the radiation is given slowly.

Human beings are already adding artificial radiation to the natural radiation they receive. In civilized countries the major source of the artificial radiation is the X-rays given in medical practice for diagnosing fractures and illnesses. The amount is not precisely known. In the United States and in Sweden it may equal the total natural dose, but is much less in this country. This would, however, add only a small fraction to the naturally-occurring mutation. Artificial radiation from the atomic and thermonuclear bombs so far exploded will contribute only a small increase to the naturally occurring radiation. But, however small the increase in the mutation rate due to artificial radiation, these mutations, like naturally occurring mutations, will nearly all interfere with normal development. They will nearly all handicap the child who receives the mutation and perhaps some of the child's descendants. Every effort should be made to cut down on all unnecessary exposure to ionizing radiation, while more is learnt about the size of the effects on mutation and the other dangers of radiation. Now that the dangers are recognized, the majority of diagnostic X-rays can be taken without giving any appreciable dose to the sex glands. In the near future, too, technical advances in radiology will make it possible to take medical X-rays involving much smaller doses of radiation.

*Direct effect of gene mutation*

The direct effect of a mutation is as yet little known. The most precisely known effects are of some mutations which alter the nature of haemoglobin. Haemoglobin is the iron containing red pigment in the red blood cells responsible for the carriage of oxygen. One of these mutations produces an altered form of haemoglobin called sickle-cell, or S haemoglobin. A man or woman with this mutant gene on one member of the chromosome pair has about equal amounts of normal and S haemoglobin. A man or woman who has this mutant gene on both members of the chromosome pair has only S haemoglobin and a little of another form of haemoglobin called foetal haemoglobin which is present in the foetus but normally disappears by about the sixth month of life. Recently, Ingram at Cambridge has shown by analysis of S haemoglobin that it differs from normal adult haemoglobin in only one of the many chemical units of which haemoglobin is built up; at one point in the structure of the complex chemical molecule of haemoglobin one aminoacid residue has been substituted for another. This change in haemoglobin probably reflects a substitution of one base in a single triplet CAT for CTT in the gene concerned. This small change in the haemoglobin molecule has important consequences. One consequence is that the solubility of S haemoglobin in its de-oxygenated form is much reduced. Children homozygous for the gene develop severe anaemia and die young from distortion of their red cells by crystallized haemoglobin. Red cells from a child with sickle-cell anaemia are shown in Plate 4a. Another consequence is that, as will be mentioned later, the altered form appears to confer protection against the invasion of the red cells by the most dangerous form of malaria parasite.

Another mutant gene whose effect is precisely known also produces a variant form of haemoglobin known as haemoglobin C. This C form has been found to differ from normal haemoglobin at the same point in the structure of the molecule as haemoglobin S, but the aminoacid substituted is a different one. A (normal) and S haemoglobin may be separated by the rate at which they move across filter paper in an electric field. Plate 4b shows the haemoglobins of a married couple, both having A and S. They have one child with only A haemoglobin and one child, severely anaemic, with only S haemoglobin. These parents could also have had AS children as shown in Figure 48.

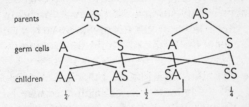

48. The possible children of two parents heterozygous for sickle-cell haemoglobin

If these two mutations are representative, they suggest that most mutations consist of single base substitutions in single triplets of DNA. These lead to single aminoacid changes in the product of the gene. The effect of such small changes may, however, be considerable.

*Gene mutations; their effect on fitness*

It has been found with animals that the great majority of mutant genes tend to lower the fitness of the animals who posses them. There are good reasons why this should be so. All gene mutations will have occurred repeatedly in the past and if a mutant gene has been favourable it will have spread through the population and become the gene, or one of the genes, most commonly present at that particular gene-locus. However, if there are large changes in the environment, it is possible that just a few mutations previously disadvantageous will have natural selective value and spread through the population. A well-established example in animals of this process is that in the common Peppered Moth. A dominant mutant gene causing a dark wing colour is rare in the moths in the beechwoods of southern England, but has become very common in the moths in the industrial north. The selective disadvantage of this gene has been shown by the fact that if light and dark forms are released in a southern beech wood, birds more readily see and eat the dark forms. In the industrial north, however, the selective balance is reversed and the majority of the Peppered Moths are coming to possess the dark gene.

Since genes interact with each other it is probable that, in general, only gene mutations of small effect can be advantageous. Further, with many gene mutations it appears that instead of the mutant gene having some new effect, it has no effect at all and such losses of activity are not likely to be advantageous. In domesticated animals and plants man has deliberately induced and selected mutations that are useful to himself. For example, the mould which produces the antibiotic penicillin, so successfully used in the treatment of certain bacterial infections, was deliberately irradiated to produce numerous new mutations. By intense selection of these mutations a domestic strain of mould has been produced which yields more penicillin and a higher proportion of the most useful form of the drug. However, if this domestic strain of the mould were released to its natural environment and it survived, most of these mutant genes would disappear as a result of natural selection and something much nearer the wild type of penicillin would develop.

In man, where an individual's fitness cannot easily be measured in his lifetime, it would be particularly difficult to detect a favourable mutation. But it is to be presumed that, as in other species, the great majority of mutations in man are disadvantageous in present circumstances. On the other hand, if any group of men and women were attempting to live in a very different environment, perhaps colonizing one of the other planets, a small proportion of mutations at present disadvantageous might be useful or even essential to the success of the venture.

## Dominant, intermediate, and recessive mutations

Disadvantageous mutant genes may have very varied effects. Firstly, there are mutant genes which produce an obvious effect even in heterozygotes, that is those who have the mutant gene on only one member of the chromosome pair. For convenience these are called dominant. An example of such a gene is the mutation which produces the thick-set dwarfs known as achondroplastic. Probably many or all of these dominant mutant genes would have even more dramatic effects in homozygotes and so they are not dominants in the strict sense that homozygotes and heterozygotes for the gene are indistinguishable. But the heterozygotes are kept so rare by natural selection that, with only one or two exceptions, homozygotes have not been reported. Secondly, there are those which show intermediate inheritance in the sense that they produce a major effect in homozygotes, but also an appreciable effect in heterozygotes. An example is the mutant gene, mentioned above, responsible for producing the sickle-cell haemoglobin instead of normal haemoglobin. Thirdly, there are recessive mutant genes, such as that responsible for fibrocystic disease of the pancreas, a children's disease described in Chapter 11, which cannot readily be detected in those heterozygous for the gene, although those who are homozygous for it may be severely affected. The distinctions between dominant, intermediate, and recessive are somewhat arbitrary, since it is probable that most apparently recessive mutant genes could be shown to have an effect in heterozygotes if we had sufficiently sensitive ways of detecting the defect. Recently, for example, the Chinese-American, Hsia, has found that the apparently normal heterozygotes for the gene responsible for phenylketonuria (the inborn error of metabolism described above in Chapter 2, page 40) cannot break down a large dose of phenylalanine quite as quickly as normal men and women. All the same, it is useful to speak of dominant and recessive mutant genes in the sense that the former produce an obvious effect in the heterozygote, and the latter an obvious effect only in those homozygous for them.

In addition to these mutant genes which always produce an effect, at any rate in homozygotes, there are many mutant genes which produce only a genetic disposition to develop some condition. Some environmental factor or the presence of other genes is also required before the mutant gene has a definite effect on development. Finally, animal experiments suggest that there are many mutant genes which produce no obvious effect, even in the homozygous state, and the presence of which can only be detected by a small reduction in average length of life.

It is the mutant genes of large effect which give rise to the malformations and diseases which provide patterns of inheritance within families similar to those Mendel found for many characters in peas. The mutant genes of small effect will provide the genetic element in the ordinary variation one sees in any population, only producing definite abnormality when many such mutant genes of minor effect happen to occur together in the same child and have a cumulative effect.

## Frequency of mutant genes in the population

The mutant genes within a population at any given moment will be composed of fresh mutations present in the germ cells that went to form the present generation and also of mutant genes which have survived and been handed down from earlier generations. There are, therefore, two factors determining the frequency of such genes in the population. One is the mutation rate and the other the average number of generations each mutation persists once it has occurred. The relative importance of the two factors varies enormously with the intensity with which natural selection is eliminating the mutant gene. This in turn depends on its nature, whether dominant or recessive, and the extent to which its effects are modified by other genes and the environment.

*Dominant mutant genes: family patterns and the frequency of conditions they cause*

Dominant genes which always produce a severe disorder in those who possess them will be very rare in the population. By the definition of dominance anyone who receives the gene will be affected by it, and this includes the children who receive it as a result of a fresh mutation. There will then be in each generation a number of children affected because of fresh mutations. The proportion of children affected from such mutations will be twice the mutation rate since each child is conceived as the result of the fusion of *two* germ cells, sperm and ovum, each of which may contain a fresh mutation. In algebraic terms, if $m$ is the mutation rate, then the proportion of children born affected from fresh mutations will be $2m$, provided that the mutation is not a cause of death in embryonic life. If none of the affected children survives to adult life and none of them has children, then the proportion of affected children in each generation will always be $2m$. The affected children will always appear sporadically, being born to unaffected parents and very nearly always having unaffected brothers and sisters. The pedigrees of the affected children will all look something like the family in Figure 49.

Since these lethal mutant genes are never passed on to the

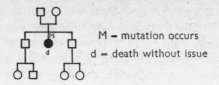

49. The family tree of a child with a condition due to a lethal dominant mutation

next generation, it is not easy to recognize that the disorder in the child is genetically determined. One clue would be that identical twins were always both affected. Another clue might be, as the late director of the Galton Laboratory in London, Penrose, has indicated, that either the mother's age, or the father's age, or sometimes both, at the birth of the child was higher than the national average. The older the patient the greater the opportunity there has been for a mutation to occur, though the size of this increased risk will vary in each sex and with the cause of the mutation.

Where an affected individual can occasionally have children it becomes possible for the dominant mutant gene to be transmitted and cause disorder in a second generation. When an individual affected by a dominant mutant gene forms germ cells, there is, as we know from the mechanism of inheritance described in Chapter 2, an even chance whether he transmits the mutant gene or a normal gene. On the average, then, half the children will be affected and half normal. In most instances the affected children will die without, in turn, having children themselves, giving pedigrees like that shown in Figure 50 with just two generations affected, one individual in the first generation and one or more children of this man or woman in the second generation.

In the pedigree two of four children are shown affected and this is the most frequent situation with four children; the

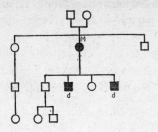

50. A family tree given by a
dominant mutant gene persist-
ing for two generations

actual probabilities with four children are: all four affected
one-sixteenth, all four normal one-sixteenth, three affected
and one normal four-sixteenths, three normal and one
affected four-sixteenths, two normal and two affected six-
sixteenths.

However, if affected individuals sometimes have children,
then it is possible for the mutant gene to be transmitted to a
third generation, though this will be exceptional if the disorder is at all serious. One will get dominant mutant genes
transmitted for many generations only if the disability they
cause is trivial or if the disorder does not come on till late in
life, when the individual who becomes affected has already
had his family.

The general relationship for conditions due to dominant
genes between the proportion of children born affected
which we will call $A$, the mutation rate, which we will call $m$,
and the fitness of those affected, which we will call $f$, is given
by the expression:

$$A = \frac{2m}{1 - f}$$

Fitness is here used in the special sense of the ratio of the
number of children born to affected individuals to the aver-

age family size in the whole population. Where those affected
never have children and so fitness is zero, then

$$A = \frac{2m}{1 - 0},$$

which is $2m$, that is to say all cases are due to fresh mutations
in each generation. Where $f$ is, say, $\frac{9}{10}$, then

$$A = \frac{2m}{1 - \frac{9}{10}},$$

which is $20m$. The number of mutant genes in the population
is stable at this figure because the $20m$ affected individuals
only replace themselves by nine-tenths and the loss exactly
balances the new cases caused by fresh mutations.

If fitness is one half, then the proportion of children born
affected will be

$$\frac{2m}{1 - \frac{1}{2}}$$

which is $4m$. These $4m$ affected individuals would be
forty in a population of a million children where $m$ was
1 in 100,000. Of these, $2m$, that is twenty (i.e. half the
total) would be born to normal parents; $m$, that is ten
(i.e. a quarter of the total) would be affected because
they were the children of the $2m$ individuals affected as a
result of mutations in the previous generation; a further
five would be affected by mutations which had come down
from the grandparental generation, and a further five would
be affected by mutant genes which had come down from the
great-grandparental generation or earlier. This means that
with conditions due to dominant mutant genes where fitness
is a half, family trees of affected individuals will look like
those in Figure 51.

The family trees will look very different with a condition
where fitness is nine-tenths and the total number of affected
individuals is $20m$ and so 200 in a population of a million
children where $m$ is 1 in 100,000. The number born to unaffected parents as a result of fresh mutations will be $2m$ or

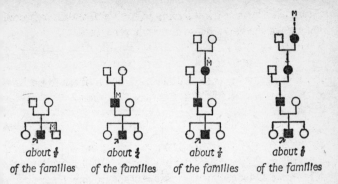

51. The typical family trees of children with a condition where 'fitness' is ½ and due to a dominant mutant gene

twenty in a million, but now this is only one-tenth of the whole number of affected individuals. The number of families with one parent, but no earlier generations affected will be $2m \times \frac{9}{10}$, that is $1\cdot8m$ or eighteen in a million. The number of families with three generations affected will be $1\cdot8m \times \frac{9}{10}$, that is $1\cdot62m$, or approximately sixteen in a million, while the remaining 146 of the total 200 affected children will have pedigrees with affected ancestors stretching back four or more generations. It should be noted, however, that even with fitness nine-tenths the proportion of individuals born affected, if $m$ is 1 in 100,000, is only 200 in a million or 1 in 5,000.

An example of dominant mutation occurring early in the eighteenth century in England and affecting certainly five, and, possibly, eleven individuals in four generations, before it died out early in the following century is shown in the family tree in Figure 52.

The condition caused by the mutation is a marked thickening of the outer horny layer of the skin, so that the skin in places is half an inch thick, black, and very rough. The first individual affected was born in 1716 at Sapiston in Suffolk.

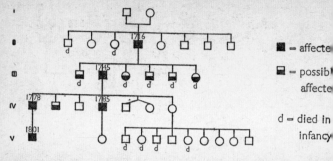

52. Penrose and Stern's pedigree of the Lambert family

He was shown to a meeting of the Royal Society in London in 1734. The affected members of the family exhibited themselves as the 'Porcupine Men', and John (IV, 1) and Richard (IV, 4) claimed that only the males in the family were affected, and that all the male descendants of II, 4 were affected. If this had been true it would have suggested (as was mentioned in Chapter 3) that the mutant gene responsible might have been on the small Y sex chromosome. However, early accounts of the 'Porcupine Men' have been re-examined and the baptismal records of the family in the parish churches of that part of Suffolk carefully searched. The new pedigree, compiled by Penrose and Stern and shown in Figure 52, suggests, that an ordinary dominant mutation affecting both sexes equally was responsible and this is consistent with the few other pedigrees of the condition which are known.

A more extensive pedigree, from Sweden, of a condition due to a dominant mutation is shown in Figure 53. The patients in this family are affected with a rare and relatively mild condition, known as transient muscular paralysis. They develop attacks of weakness, in most cases at least once a week, lasting for a few minutes up to an hour. Sometimes only one limb is weak, sometimes the whole limb and trunk

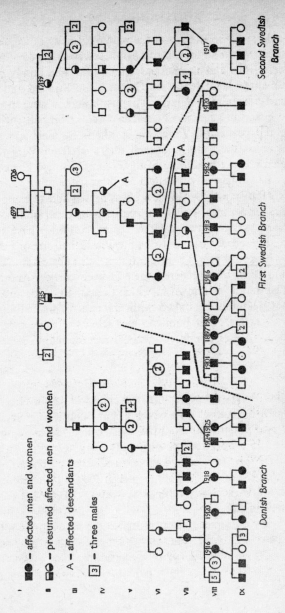

- = affected men and women

 = presumed affected men and women

A = affected descendants

3 = three males

Second Swedish Branch

First Swedish Branch

Danish Branch

53. Part of Gamstorp's pedigree of hereditary transient muscular paralysis

musculature is so weak that the patient, if lying down, cannot turn over or sit up without help. However, the condition is not serious and the patients can work. The family was picked up independently by Gamstorp in Sweden and by Helweg-Larsen in Denmark. The two branches were shown to be linked in generation III. The Swedish branch derives from the parish of Vanga in southern Sweden and the ancestor of the Danish branch migrated from Vanga to Denmark at the beginning of the present century. The condition has apparently no effect on fitness, the family is unusually fertile, and Dr Gamstorp was herself able to examine no less than ninety-one living patients in generations VII, VIII, and IX. Since two members of generation II have had affected descendants, it is to be presumed that one or other of the ancestral pair, i.e. generation I, was affected and that the mutation had occurred then or even earlier. Another Swedish family is known in which the condition occurs. It cannot definitely be linked with Gamstorp's main family, but, since this other family comes from the same part of Sweden, an illegitimate connexion with the main family is probable.

*Children homozygous for a dominant mutant gene*

It will only very rarely occur that a child will be born homozygous for a mutant gene which has any considerable effect in heterozygotes. For example, even where fitness is nine-tenths, the proportion of germ cells carrying the mutation either fresh or transmitted from an affected parent will be $10m$, that is 1 in 10,000 where $m$ is 1 in 100,000. The random chance of two such germ cells meeting is $(1/10,000)^2$ or 1 in a hundred million.

The few examples known of marriages between a couple each heterozygous for the same dominant mutant gene suggest that these may often severely affect those homozygous for these genes. Two Norwegian parents, each with a dominant mutant gene for short fingers, had a child with a very severe general disturbance of the skeleton. Two American parents each with a dominant mutant gene for pin-point sized abnormalities of the capillaries in the skin and mucous membranes, had a child with large and severe abnormalities of the blood-vessels.

## CHAPTER 9

# More about Gene Mutations

*Frequency and dangers of recessive mutant genes*

THE relation between the mutation rate and the proportion of individuals in the population with disorders caused by recessive mutant genes is similar to that for disorders due to dominant mutant genes, but it is much less likely that the population will be in genetic balance. If there is genetic balance, the proportion of individuals born genetically predisposed to develop the disorder is, using the same symbols as with dominants,

$$A = \frac{m}{1 - f}.$$

This may be compared with the relationship for dominant genes, which was

$$A = \frac{2m}{1 - f}.$$

The two-fold difference is due to the fact that whenever an affected individual dies without having children two of the recessive mutant genes are eliminated, instead of one as with dominants. So the fresh mutations entering the population are balanced by the failure to reproduce of half the number of affected individuals.

The gene frequencies in the population, however, are very different in recessive genes and so are the family trees. When a fresh mutation occurs and the mutant gene is recessive, one does not know that the mutation has occurred. With very few exceptions the germ cell containing the new mutant gene will fuse with a germ cell containing a normal form of the gene, and the resulting child will be heterozygous for the mutant gene. By the definition of recessive the heterozygous individual shows no effects of the mutant gene. He or she will have the same chance of having children as anyone else in the population and, when reproducing, will transmit the recessive mutant gene to half the children. These children who receive the mutant gene will, in nearly all instances, receive a normal gene from the other parent and so again be unaffected heterozygotes. The unseen state of affairs will be as shown in the family tree in Figure 54 where the unknown carriers are represented by a spot in the male and female symbols.

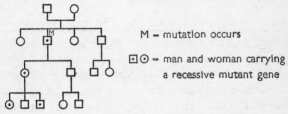

M - mutation occurs

⊡ ⊙ - man and woman carrying a recessive mutant gene

54. The course taken by a recessive mutant gene

If they are truly recessive there will be no selection against these mutant genes in carriers and so they will normally be transmitted for many generations. As new mutations constantly occur in each generation the frequency of recessive mutant genes reaches quite a high level in the population. It has, admittedly very roughly, been estimated that each of us are heterozygous for an average of three recessive mutant genes, each of which in the homozygous condition would cause severe disability. No trouble is caused by these recessive mutants till two individuals are unlucky enough to marry when each happens to be heterozygous for the same recessive gene. Then, from the mechanism of inheritance, there is an even chance whether each parent transmits the mutant gene or the normal gene, and the risks for the children are shown in the family tree in Figure 55.

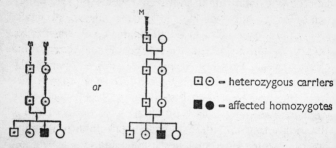

55. The offspring of a couple heterozygous for the same recessive mutant gene

With a family of two children the probabilities of the different possible combinations of affected and unaffected are given by the expansion of the expression $(\frac{3}{4} + \frac{1}{4})^2$. On the average, nine times in sixteen such parents have no affected child and their carrier state remains unknown, six times out of sixteen they have one affected and one normal child, and only one time out of sixteen are they unlucky enough to have two affected children and no normal child. The expected proportion of families with one child affected to those with two children affected is six to one. In practice it is often somewhat less, since families with no affected children are not very readily picked up. For example, in a consecutive series of thirty-six patients with fibrocystic disease of the pancreas attending a London children's hospital and coming from two-child families it was found that in twenty-nine instances one child was affected and in seven instances both were affected.

Unfortunately, the majority of disorders due to the homozygous state of a recessive gene are serious and at the moment difficult to treat. In most instances, affected individuals will not reproduce and the family tree will show one or two children in a family affected, with no one affected in earlier or later generations. Even if an affected individual does have children, though he or she will transmit the gene to all the children, these children will all be heterozygous carriers and unaffected, unless, by an unlucky chance, the other parent is also a carrier of the same gene. Where fitness is zero, and the mutant gene is truly recessive, the carrier frequency will settle to a level such that sufficient affected children are born and fail to reproduce to offset the fresh mutations coming in with each generation. That is $A = m$.

Once frequency of affected individuals is known, the proportion of the population who are heterozygous for the gene may be deduced from the formula put forward by Hardy and Weinberg (see Chapter 4, page 67). For example, the frequency of phenylketonuria in this country is estimated to be about 1 in 40,000. With marriage at random this frequency implies that as many as 1 in 100 or 0·01 of the population are carriers, since if $q$ is the gene-frequency of the recessive gene responsible, $q^2 = 1/40,000$, $q = 1/200$ and the proportion of the population who are heterozygous carriers of the gene is $2pq$, that is

$$2 \times \frac{1}{200} \times \frac{199}{200}$$

which is approximately 1 in 100. It is because there are very many genes of this type that it is probable that most of us are carriers for one or more of them.

The assumption of marriage occurring at random is nearly true for most parts of Britain today. The proportion of first cousin marriages is probably less than four in a thousand. There are parts of the world, for example Japanese villages, where as many as 8 per cent of all marriages are between first cousins. In a marriage between blood relations the chance of both a husband and wife carrying the same recessive gene is much increased. If the husband has a particular recessive gene, for example the gene for phenylketonuria, the chance that his first cousin wife also has the gene because of the blood relationship is one in eight. This is much higher than the one in a hundred risk that an unrelated woman would be a carrier and can be explained as follows: if a husband A has a particular recessive gene the chance that it came from the parent through whom he is related to his wife (in Figure 56 this parent is his mother), rather than the other parent is one half. If his mother has it, then the chance that her brother or sister also has it is, by the mechanism of inheritance, one half. If this mother's brother also has it the chance that he will pass it on to a child is also one half. The total chance, then, that the wife will have the same recessive gene is $\frac{1}{2} \times \frac{1}{2} \times \frac{1}{2}$; that is one in eight. This is illustrated in Figure 56. The wife could also have received a similar recessive mutant gene by chance, but this risk is relatively small if the gene is uncommon.

56. The chance that a wife will have a gene carried by her husband if they are first cousins

It is, therefore, not unusual to find that the parents of children with disorders due to recessive genes are blood relations, for example first cousins. It is found that about 1 in 20 of the parents of children with phenylketonuric defect are first cousins, as compared with the 4 in 1,000 first cousin marriages in the general population. The rarer the condition, the more likely it is that the parents of an affected child are carriers of the same mutant gene because of a blood relationship, rather than carriers of two similar but independently mutating genes. Also the rarer the condition, the more probable it is that families in which it occurs are related to each other, even though this relationship is often not known to the families. Sweden is particularly well suited for genetic research into lines of ancestry because of the excellently kept system of parish registers. Recently Sjögren and Larsson of Stockholm have studied fourteen patients, in eleven families, with severe mental defect associated with spastic limbs and scaly red skin. Another fourteen members of these families had been similarly affected, but were no longer alive. They found that in six of the eleven families, more than half, the parents were blood relations. They also found that almost all the patients had one or more ancestral lines leading back to a few couples living in the north-eastern coastal district of Sweden in the early years of the eighteenth century.

Part of the pedigrees are reproduced in Figure 57 which shows how four of the families, into which thirteen affected individuals have been born since 1880, lead back to two of these ancestral couples. The most probable path by which the mutant gene has travelled down the generations is shown in the pedigree by marking in the probable carriers. Sometimes there are alternative paths. It is very likely, too, that one of each of the two ancestral pairs shown (Olaf T. born 1705 and Gunilla J. born 1708, and Pehr J. born 1710 and Dordi O. born 1717) was a carrier. There is evidence of other carriers in this area at that time. Sjögren and Larsson estimate that the original gene mutation may have occurred as early as the fourteenth century, a mutation which was responsible for the birth of nearly thirty individuals with grave handicaps some five centuries later.

The British eye specialist, Sorsby, has recently drawn attention to a very early report of a cousin marriage leading to the birth of a child with a condition due to a recessive gene. The report is of the birth of the Jewish patriarch Noah, who built the Ark and survived the Flood. The report is found in the Book of Enoch, which was lost until three manuscripts in Ethiopian were brought out of Abyssinia in 1773. It is

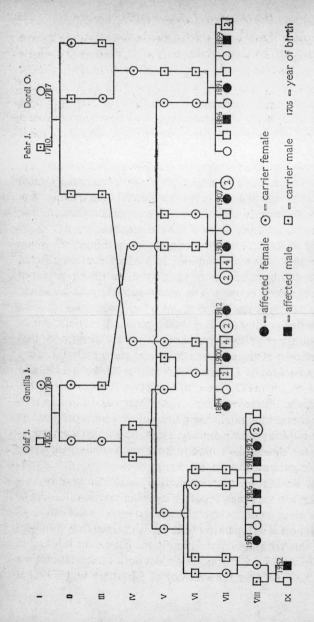

57. Part of Sjögren and Larsson's pedigree of mental defect with spastic limbs and scaly red skin

● = affected female   ⊙ = carrier female   1705 = year of birth
■ = affected male   ☐ = carrier male

thought to have been written in the second and first centuries B.C. The description of Noah's birth in the English translation reads:

> She became pregnant and brought forth a child, the flesh of which was white as snow, and red as a rose; the hair of whose head was white, like wool and long; and whose eyes were beautiful. When he opened them he illuminated all the house, like the sun.

Sorsby notes that, once the laudatory commendations are disregarded, this is an unequivocal description of an albino. Neither Genesis nor the Book of Enoch give details of the blood-relationship between Noah's parents, Lamech and Betenos, but in the Book of Jubilee it is stated that they were first cousins. The extent to which Noah and his parents are historical figures is uncertain; but the authors of the traditions recorded in the Book of Enoch certainly knew of albinism. If we are all descended from Noah and there has been no selection against the gene for albinism one would expect a quarter of the world's population to be albinos!

The effect of cousin marriages and other inbreeding on recessive mutant genes in a balanced population is to reduce their frequency. The reason is that a rather lower carrier frequency is needed than with random marriage to produce sufficient affected children to balance the fresh mutations coming into the population. Changes in the cousin marriage rate will temporarily unbalance the relation between affected individuals and the mutation rate. If the amount of inbreeding is increased, then the proportion of affected children born will become higher than that which balances the input of fresh mutations. This will, however, gradually cut down the frequency of the recessive mutant genes in the population and the carrier rate until once more the proportion of affected children is

$$A = \frac{m}{1 - f}$$

In the same way, if, as has happened in Britain over the past three generations, the amount of inbreeding decreases, then for a time the frequency of children born homozygous for and so affected by recessive mutant genes will fall. The carrier frequency, however, will in consequence slowly increase until the proportion of affected children once again reaches the original level, and the balance between loss and input of the mutant genes is restored.

Any selective effect on the gene in the heterozygous condition is, however, much more important than changes in the amount of inbreeding, in affecting the balance between mutation rate and the proportion of children born homozygous for recessive genes. It may well be that few genes are completely recessive. If the mutant gene has to some extent a disadvantageous effect in the heterozygote, then the gene is really behaving as dominant. Selection against the heterozygotes even though mild will determine the frequency of the mutant gene and will keep the gene frequency down to a level such that homozygotes must be extremely rare. For example, even with the high mutation rate of 1 in 10,000 and a fitness of 0·9, the frequency of heterozygotes from the formula for dominance,

$$A = \frac{2m}{1 - f}$$

will be 1/500, the gene frequency 1/1,000 and the frequency of perhaps severely affected homozygotes only 1 in a million.

There are also, however, at least three mutant genes which in the homozygous state cause children to die young, but which are not uncommon. If the only selective force at work was the death in childhood of the homozygotes, then, after making allowances for any change in inbreeding, the homozygotes should have a frequency fairly closely related to the mutation rate, and these not uncommon disorders would imply very high mutation rates. The three conditions are:

sickle-cell anaemia, which in parts of Africa and India affects about 1 child born in 100 and is due to the homozygous state of the mutant gene producing S haemoglobin to which we have previously referred (Chapter 8, page 158); Mediterranean anaemia, which in parts of Italy affects about 1 child in 100 and is due to the homozygous state of a gene which does not produce an abnormal haemoglobin but interferes with the production of normal haemoglobin; fibrocystic disease of the pancreas, which in Britain and North America affects about 1 child in 2,000 (an account of fibrocystic disease of the pancreas is given in Chapter 11).

To explain these high frequencies the ingenious suggestion has been made that those who are heterozygous for these genes have some selective advantage over 'normal' individuals who do not possess them at all. We know the nature of this advantage only in the gene for sickle-cell anaemia. It was noticed that the frequency of this gene, which can easily be recognized in the heterozygote, often paralleled the amount of infection with malignant tertian malaria, to which the population has been subjected. The parts of the world in which sickle-cell anaemia is common are shown in Figure 58; all are malarious. It therefore appeared that babies who were heterozygotes for the sickle-cell gene were more resistant to this parasite than were 'normal' babies and that fewer of them died of this type of malaria. It would need only a relatively small selective advantage of this kind to balance the death of homozygotes. For example, in a community where the gene frequency is $0.1$ and marriage is at random, the proportion of children dying from the anaemia is $(0.1)^2$, that is $0.01$ (1 per cent), the carrier frequency is $0.18$ (18 per cent) and the proportion of individuals homozygous for the normal gene is $0.81$ (81 per cent). This means that there are nine of the mutant genes in the heterozygous state for every one in the homozygous state: there are nine and not eighteen since homozygotes have two mutant genes.

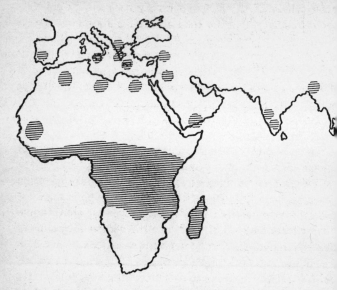

58. The parts of the world where sickle-cell anaemia is common (after H. Lehmann)

A balanced population with the observed gene frequency would be established, though all the homozygotes died young, if the fitness of heterozygotes was 10/9 and that of 'normals' was 80/81. The germ cells forming the next generation would then include 0·8 (derived as in Table 13) with the normal gene $N$, produced by normal men and women, together with 0·1 containing the normal gene and 0·1 containing the sickle-cell gene produced by heterozygotes. This is illustrated in Figure 59.

These germ cells would replace exactly the parent generation, with 0·81 $NN$, 0·18 $NS$, and 0·01 $SS$, and once again give one in a hundred children born with sickle-cell anaemia. This is shown in Figure 60.

| Parents' genotypes | 0·81 NN | 0·18 NS | 0·01 SS |
| Relative fertility | $(\frac{80}{81})$ | $(\frac{10}{9})$ | (0) |
| Germ-cell frequencies | 0.8 N | 0·1 N<br>0·1 S | none |

59. Selective advantage of the heterozygote for gene $S$ balancing the early death of $SS$ homozygotes

*One germ cell*

|  | (0·9)N | (0·1)S |
|---|---|---|
| (0·9)N | (0·81) NN | (0·09)NS |
| (0·1)S | (0·09)NS | (0·01)SS |

*Other germ cell*

60. Parental genotypes formed by germ cells of which $\frac{9}{10}$ carry $N$ and $\frac{1}{10}$ carry $S$

Presumably, a similar advantage is possessed, or was possessed at some time in the past, by the heterozygotes for the gene, which in homozygotes caused Mediterranean anaemia in the Po delta in Italy and other districts where the disease is common; but we have no idea, yet, what the advantage might be. Similarly, we have no evidence of the nature of the advantage conferred by the gene for fibrocystic disease of the pancreas in north European populations.

Once the selective advantage of the heterozygote is lost, one would expect the frequency of the gene to fall gradually from the death of homozygotes till a balance is reached with the mutation rate. Negroes in North America where there is no malaria have a frequency of the sickle-cell gene lower than that of the West African populations from which they originated. The difference (after allowing for the 30 per cent of white admixture) is just about what one would expect from ten generations of deaths of homozygotes, with no counterbalancing advantage of heterozygotes.

## Risks of cousin marriage

The extent to which the average member of the population is heterozygous for the kind of recessive genes which cause malformations or illness in those homozygous for them determines the general risk to the children of cousin marriages. To take a theoretical example: if the average individual is heterozygous for four such recessive genes, a pair of cousins will have, on the average, one of these genes in common and the average risk to the children of being homozygous will be one in four. Information on a large scale is only available at the moment for illness at birth and in the first few years of life. This comes from a survey made under the direction of the Americans, Neel and Schull, by the Atomic Bomb Casualty Commission in Japan, and a survey in France by Sutter and Tabah. Both surveys indicate that the risks of death in infancy and early childhood are about doubled among the offspring of first cousin marriages. The findings for Hiroshima (women who experienced significant radiation were not included) are shown in Table 15.

## Sex-linked recessive mutations: the family patterns and the frequency of the conditions they cause

Where disorders are due to recessive mutations on the unmatched part of the $X$ chromosome (see Chapter 3), the relationship between gene frequency and the proportion of children born affected in the population is much modified. The relationships are intermediate between those for dominant mutations and those for ordinary recessives on the auto-

Table 15. Deaths in infancy and early childhood for cousin
and unrelated marriages: data from Hiroshima

| | PARENTS' RELATIONSHIP | | | |
|---|---|---|---|---|
| | *First cousins* | *First cousins once removed* | *Second cousins* | *Unrelated* |
| Total infants | 352 | 106 | 144 | 567 |
| Total deaths | 41 | 9 | 8 | 31 |
| Deaths per cent | 11·6 | 8·5 | 5·6 | 5·5 |

somes. A truly recessive sex-linked mutant of this kind is not
subject to selection in a girl or woman heterozygous for it,
since, in the presence of the normal alternative form of the
gene on the other sex chromosome, it has no effect on development. In a boy or man, however, it is fully subject to
selection.

The proportion of males, who are, of course, only about
half the population, born genetically predisposed to develop
disorders due to sex-linked recessive mutations is, using the
same symbols as before,

$$A = \frac{3m}{1-f}$$

and so the proportion of the whole population born predisposed is, approximately,

$$A = \frac{1\frac{1}{2}m}{1-f}$$

This may be compared with

$$\frac{2m}{1-f}$$

for conditions due to dominant mutant genes and

$$\frac{m}{1-f}$$

for recessive mutant genes. Girls and women will only be affected by a sex-linked recessive gene when they are homozygous for it, which will happen rarely if the fitness of the affected males is low. It would require both that the ovum contains the mutant gene, either because the mother is a carrier or from a fresh mutation, and that the sperm cell contains the mutant gene either because the father, though affected, has survived to have children or from a fresh mutation. However, on two occasions recently girls have been born with the classic bleeding disease haemophilia, in which the time the blood takes to clot is much prolonged.

The fate of a fresh sex-linked recessive mutation depends initially on whether it occurs in a sperm or an ovum. Only a half of all sperms contain an $X$ chromosome, so that, if $m$ is the mutation rate, only $\dfrac{m}{2}$ sperms will contain an $X$ chromosome with a fresh mutation. These sperms will always produce girls and the ova they fertilize will almost invariably contain an $X$ chromosome with the normal alternative form of the gene, so that a heterozygous carrier girl will result. One will not know that the mutation has taken place. However, once this woman has children the mutant gene may show itself in the second generation. Half the ova the woman forms will have the $X$ chromosome with the mutant gene, the other half will contain the $X$ chromosome with the normal alternative gene. If the ovum with the mutant gene meets a sperm with an $X$ chromosome, the child will be a girl who is a carrier like her mother. If the ovum meets a sperm with a $Y$ chromosome, however, the child will be a boy with no normal gene on his $Y$ chromosome corresponding to the mutant gene on his $X$ chromosome and will have his development affected. If the condition is a serious one this boy will probably die without having any children. A carrier sister of this boy will be unaffected but likely to have affected boys. The type of family tree which may develop is shown in Figure 61.

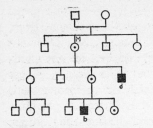

61. A typical family tree produced by a sex-linked recessive mutant gene

The women who are heterozygous for the gene in such pedigrees, if the gene is truly recessive, are only recognizable by the fact that they have affected boys.

If an affected male survives, however, and has children, the genetic type of his children is certain. If he transmits his *Y* chromosome, he automatically fails to transmit the mutant gene, and his boys do not possess it and can not transmit it to their children. If he transmits his *X* chromosome he will produce a girl who is heterozygous for the mutant gene. The situation is shown in Figure 62.

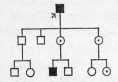

62. The descendants of a man who has a sex-linked recessive gene

In the rare event of an affected man marrying a woman who is a carrier, half the daughters, on the average, would be heterozygotes and half homozygotes, since the father can only transmit the mutant gene and the mother has an equal chance of transmitting the mutant gene or its normal equivalent. The chances for their children are as in Figure 63.

63. The offspring of a man with a
sex-linked recessive gene, whose wife
carries the same gene

If a homozygous affected woman survives to have children, all her sons must be affected and all her daughters must
be carriers, since she can only transmit $X$ chromosomes with
the mutant gene. It is possible, particularly in populations
in which the average size of the family is small, for a recessive mutant gene to be transmitted for several generations through heterozygous women before an affected boy
appears.

If the mutation appears first on an $X$ chromosome in an
ovum its fate will depend on whether it meets an $X$- or a $Y$-
bearing sperm. In the former case the child will be a carrier
girl and the family pattern ensuing will be the same as that
for a carrier girl produced by a mutation occurring in an
$X$-bearing sperm. In the latter case a boy will be produced
and this boy will at once be affected, and if the condition is
serious the mutation will probably not be transmitted further.
If the affected man does survive to have children all his
daughters will be carriers and, on the average, half his
daughters' sons affected, but his own sons will be unaffected
and cannot transmit the condition.

The relationship between the proportion of women who
are heterozygous carriers of sex-linked recessive mutations
and the frequency of affected boys is straightforward, if the
fitness of the affected boys is nil. The proportion of boys
affected from fresh mutations is the mutation rate in ova,
that is $m$, and in addition there will be, if the fitness is nil, a
further $2m$ affected boys born to carrier mothers. This, in a
population which is replacing itself, implies that the proportion of carrier mothers is $4m$, since they will average only a
son each and only half of these are affected. At these fre-

quencies the proportion of carrier women is stable. The $4m$
mothers will replace themselves, on the average, by a girl each,
of whom a half, that is $2m$, will also be carriers. The proportion of women who are carriers from fresh mutations is $2m$,
since they each have two $X$ chromosomes on which a mutation
may have occurred, giving $4m$ in all. Several investigators have
found that about 1 child in 25,000 develops a severe muscle
disorder called the Duchenne type of muscular dystrophy.
This affects young children, leads to invalidism before the
teens, and, usually, death in the early twenties. The proportion of children who have the illness shows that the mutation
rate is about 1 in 75,000, and that the proportion of women
who are carriers is about 1 in 19,000. Duchenne muscular
dystrophy is described in Chapter 11.

It follows that with a condition of this kind one-third of
the boys affected are the product of fresh mutations. Here
the mother is not a carrier and so no relatives, not even
brothers, will be effected. Another third of boys will be
affected because their mother was the recipient of a fresh
mutation. Here brothers are at risk and sisters may be
carriers, but none of the mother's brothers will be affected
or the mother's sisters be carriers. Another sixth will be
affected because of a mutation which occurred in a germ cell
going to form the mother's mother, which has been transmitted to the mother. Here the mother's brothers as well as
the patient's brothers may be affected and the mother's
sisters may be carriers. The remaining sixth will be affected
because of mutations occurring in germ cells going to form
the mother's mother's mother, or earlier still. The frequency
of the different types is shown in Figure 64.

Accordingly, it is not at all uncommon to find no relatives
affected with conditions due to sex-linked recessive mutant
genes which severely reduce fitness. Not only will boys
affected by fresh mutations, as in family A, have no brothers
affected, but families of the second type B, where only the

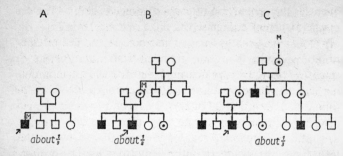

64. The typical distribution of the families of boys with a severe condition due to a sex-linked recessive mutant gene

mother is a carrier, have often only one affected boy. This is
particularly true in these days of small families. One finds in
practice that the proportion of brothers of patients affected
is not half, which it would be if all mothers of such patients
were carriers, but about a third. This is made up of one-third
of patients where brothers are not at risk, and two-
thirds where the risk for brothers is a half. In the same way,
mother's brothers are at risk only where the mother's mother
is a carrier, and so one finds only about one-sixth of these
affected.

With milder conditions, where affected men can have
children, the proportion of carrier women in the population
is higher in relation to the mutation rate. For example, where
fitness is two-thirds, the proportion of boys born affected
would be $9m$, of which $m$ would come from fresh mutations
and the remaining $8m$ be born to the $16m$ carrier women. Of
these carrier women, $6m$ would be the daughters of affected
men, $8m$ daughters of carrier women, and $2m$ affected by
fresh mutations. Where affected men can have children it
will be more usual for a sex-linked recessive mutant gene to
survive many generations.

Figure 65 shows part of an extensive and unusually fertile

Swiss family in which a single sex-linked recessive mutation occurring about the end of the sixteenth century in the town of Tenna has been transmitted through eleven generations. The disease in this family, called Christmas disease or haemophilia B, is quite distinct from classical haemophilia, or haemophilia A, but like it is due to a clotting defect of the blood and is caused by a sex-linked recessive mutant gene. The illnesses are distinct in that the disturbance in the mechanism of blood clotting is different. Blood serum from a haemophilia A patient will correct the clotting defect of haemophilia B blood and vice versa. The genes concerned are also distinct in that each type breeds true within a family, for example haemophilia B in this family.

The family was first reported in the medical literature in 1837 by Thormann, who looked after one of the affected members and knew that the condition was transmitted from grandfathers to grandsons through women who were then known as 'conductors', and whom we would now call carriers. In all, some fifty-five men have been affected in this family and the Polish doctor, Moor-Jankowski, and his Swiss colleagues who brought this family tree up to date were able to test by modern methods eleven living affected males, as well as to prove the point that the carrier women are in no way abnormal on any of the laboratory tests yet available.

The woman in generation I (U.W., married in 1669 to A.W. of Tenna) was certainly a 'conductor'. Not only was her son S.W. (born 1676, died 1741, II, 3 in the diagram) the first man in the family to be recorded in the church register as a bleeder, but her daughter U.W. (born 1678, died 1757, II, 4), was certainly a carrier since she had 3 affected sons. The mutant gene has passed down mostly through carrier women, but sometimes through affected men, until fourteen boys and men in the family are affected in the present generation. This family is exceptional in its fertility, so that the re-

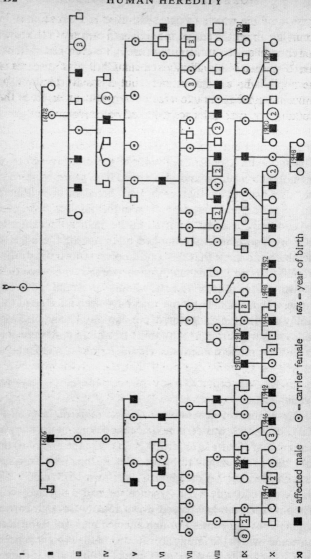

65. Part of Moor-Jankowski, Truog, and Huser's pedigree of haemophilia B (Christmas disease)

■ = affected male    ⊙ = carrier female    1676 = year of birth

duction of the fitness in the men affected estimated to be about 40 per cent has been more than matched by the exceptional fertility of the carrier women. The fertility of these carrier women is actually greater than that of the women in the family who are not carriers, but it would, perhaps, be unwise to attribute this to some advantage conferred by the mutant gene, with evidence from only a single family.

# CHAPTER 10

# *Chromosome Abnormalities in Man*

GENE or point mutations involve a very small section of a chromosome. Disturbances of the mechanism of inheritance may occur involving a considerable part of a chromosome or even a whole chromosome. These have been studied in considerable detail in plants and animals, but only very recently in man. The fruitfly and other two-winged flies are particularly suited for studies of this kind as the chromosomes in their salivary glands are relatively enormous. The loss of as little as a thousandth part of one of the larger chromosomes may be recognized. With present techniques it would only be possible to recognize loss of the order of a tenth of one of the larger chromosomes in human beings.

Animal studies have shown that the loss of an appreciable fragment, say a fifth, of a large chromosome is usually not compatible with life. The presence of extra fragments of chromosome, however, may not kill the embryo, though it causes abnormal development. A number of examples are known, in various species of plant, of individuals with a whole extra chromosome. These individuals are known as 'trisomics', since one chromosome is present in triplicate, instead of as a pair. For example, *Datura stramonium* (the thorn apple) has twelve pairs of chromosomes. All twelve possible trisomics are viable, have been identified, and all show characteristic variations from the normal plant.

## *Origin of trisomics and monosomics; non-disjunction*

It is easy to understand how trisomics and monosomics can arise. The process is perhaps more natural than the fragmentation of chromosomes which leads to deficiencies, reduplications, or exchanges of parts of chromosomes. All that is required is a failure of the mechanism by which one member of each pair of chromosome passes into the germ-cell; this failure of a chromosome pair to separate is called 'non-disjunction'. If both members of a pair enter a germ cell, then at fertilization a third chromosome of that pair is introduced, resulting in a trisomic. If neither member of a pair enters the germ cell, then the chromosome introduced by the other germ cell at fertilization has no partner and a monosomic is produced.

The first trisomics to be recognized in animals were fruit-flies trisomic for the pair of genes determining sex. In the fruitfly, as in man, sex is largely determined by a pair of sex chromosomes, females having the genetic constitution $XX$ and males the genetic constitution $XY$. The American, Bridges, in 1916 noticed some peculiar patterns of inheritance for genes linked to the $X$ chromosome in certain strains of fruitfly. He made the brilliant suggestion that these exceptional females were trisomic for the sex chromosomes, having the genetic constitution $XXY$. Examination later of the chromosomes of those flies showed that his deductions were correct. Since then fruitflies which were $XXX$ have been identified, though these are much less viable than $XXY$ flies. Also flies monosomic for the $X$ chromosome, genetically $X$ nothing (usually written $XO$) have been found; these are males. It is postulated that because of the normal sex differences, animals and plants are more tolerant of variations in the number of sex chromosomes than of the other chromosomes. However, trisomics and monosomics for the very small fourth chromosome have also been recognized in the fruitfly.

*Trisomics and monosomics in man*

As recorded in Chapter 2, it was only in 1956 that cytologists were able to make preparations showing the chromosomes in man sufficiently well for their number to be counted. These methods have been steadily improved in the last few years, particularly by British scientists of the Medical Research Council's unit at Harwell. Satisfactory preparations may now be made from bone marrow cells, white blood cells, or skin cells. The cells are encouraged to grow in the laboratory, then treated with a substance called colchicine which tends to slow cell division at a stage when the chromosomes are well spread out, then killed and stained.

## Abnormalties of the sex chromosomes in man

Two interesting conditions had been recognized for some years by medical practitioners where there was reason to suppose that abnormalities of sexual development were associated with abnormalities of the sex chromosomes. The first group of patients, said to have Klinefelter's syndrome, are apparent males characterized by undeveloped testes, relative absence of facial, axillary, and pubic hair, often some degree of mammary gland development, and a feminine distribution of fat. They are males who are somewhat feminine in their development. They are usually, perhaps always, sterile and many of them are first recognized in clinics for the investigation and treatment of sterility in men. These patients are often, but by no means always, mentally retarded, and have come to notice also among children in schools for the educationally subnormal. The second group of patients, said to have Turner's syndrome, are apparent females, characterized by a failure to mature sexually, undeveloped gonads, dwarfism, webbing of the neck with a low hair-line, often deafness, and a malformation of the heart. These patients are mostly of normal intelligence.

For the past ten years, a relatively rough and ready method of sexing has been available which depends on simple relatively low-power microscopy of cells, such as those in scrapings from the inner side of the cheek. In females, but ot in males, a spot of dark-staining material may be seen in many cells at the edge of the nucleus. Those with this spot are said to be 'chromatin positive' and it is thought that the condition must depend on the presence of two $X$ chromosomes, one of which is inactive and takes up stain. Most patients with Klinefelter's syndrome, though externally male, were found to be chromatin positive and so, presumably, had two $X$ chromosomes, while most patients with Turner's syndrome were found to be chromatin negative, and so, presumably, had only one $X$ chromosome. This was confirmed by the finding that patients with Turner's syndrome could have conditions which are known to be determined by recessive genes on the $X$ chromosome, such as the common forms of colour-blindness. It was first thought that Klinefelter's syndrome patients simply had the female sex chromosome pair $XX$, and Turner's syndrome the male sex chromosome pair $XY$, and that, for unknown reasons, there had been some partial reversal of sex development in embryonic life in each case. But the new technique of chromosome counting showed that the underlying abnormality was really more interesting.

Early in 1959 in this country workers at Harwell and at Edinburgh were able to show that patients with Klinefelter's syndrome had not 46, but 47 chromosomes. They were trisomic for the sex chromosomes, having the genetic constitution $XXY$. Patients with Turner's syndrome, on the other hand, had not 46 but 45 chromosomes. They were monosomic for the sex chromosomes, having a single $X$ chromosome and so being genetically $XO$. The ways in which non-disjunction of the sex chromosomes could produce the two syndromes are shown in Figure 66.

Patients with Klinefelter's syndrome could result from the non-disjunction of the sex chromosomes in sperm-cell formation resulting in a sperm with both $X$ and $Y$ chromosomes which on fertilizing a normal $X$-bearing egg cell, would give

an *XXY* embryo. Alternatively, if non-disjunction occurred
in egg-cell formation, an egg cell with two *X* chromosomes
would result, which on fertilization with a normal *Y*-bearing

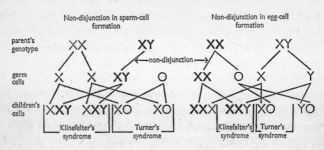

66. To show the production of children with genotypes *XXY*, *XXX*
and *XO* as a result of the failure of the sex chromosomes to separate
in germ-cell formation

sperm cell would again give an *XXY* embryo but on fertilization with a normal *X*-bearing sperm would give an *XXX* embryo. Patients with Turner's syndrome could be affected as a
result of non-disjunction in sperm-cell formation producing a
sperm with no sex chromosomes. On fertilizing a normal egg
cell this would give an *XO* embryo and Turner's syndrome.
Alternatively, Turner's syndrome could be due to non-
disjunction in egg-cell formation giving an egg cell with no
sex chromosomes; on fertilization by a normal *X*-bearing
specimen this would give an *XO* embryo, and on fertilization
with a normal *Y*-bearing sperm cell could give an *YO* embryo. It will be seen that non-disjunction of the sex chromosomes in the formation of an egg cell can give rise to two
new genetic constitutions, *XXX* and *YO*. There is reason to
suppose that *YO*, involving a deficiency of the large *X*
chromosome, would be lethal, as it is in the fruitfly. The
*XXX* constitution, however, has been found several times
in near normal women.

It is interesting that, though the sex chromosome abnormalities in man parallel those in the fruitfly, the details of sex determination are different. The $Y$ chromosome appears to have little function in the fruitfly. The $XXY$ individual is a fertile female, the $XO$ individual is a male, so that two $X$ chromosomes produce a female and one $X$ a male. In contrast, the $XXY$ human is a modified male and the $XO$ human a modified female. In man the little $Y$ chromosome appears to be the prime determinant of masculinity.

Recently men have been found with an $XYY$ genotype. The full range of manifestation of this genotype is not yet known, but it can predispose to tall stature, mental retardation and aggressive behaviour.

## Mongolism: trisomic state of one of the smallest chromosomes

No monosomics have yet been found for any of the other 22 chromosome pairs, but three trisomics for autosomes have already been found and one of these is of considerable importance in medical practice.

Over a century ago, an English physician, Langdon Down, distinguished a group of imbeciles and idiots, whom he was able to recognize by their physical peculiarities. He called the condition in these patients 'mongolism'. This is perhaps an unfortunate term as their resemblance to members of the Mongolian races is only superficial and there is no real association. Like patients with Klinefelter's syndrome, mongols are not uncommon and constitute about 2 in a thousand live-born children in western Europe and North America. Turner's syndrome in contrast is rare. The characteristic physical features in mongols may occur individually in normal children, but only occur together in mongolism. These features include a small round head, small eye-openings which are somewhat slanting and have a persistent fold of skin over their inner edge, a small bridge to the nose, a small mouth without the normal cupid's bowing of the lips, small simply formed ears, short fingers with an especially short second segment of the little finger, and general laxity of the joints. There are also more detailed characters one may recognize in the pattern of the iris and in prints taken from the palm of the hand. Certain internal malformations, in particular malformations of the heart, are also common in mongol children. The degree of mental defect varies, but only a few are suited to schools for the educationally subnormal and most come under the care of the local health authority. Although the condition is most often recognized in western Europe and North America, where it contributes a substantial proportion of all imbecile children who survive to school age, it also occurs in the Mongolian and African races.

Since the first description, many clues to the cause of mongolism have been found. Mongol children usually occur sporadically in an otherwise normal family, and there is no special tendency for other types of malformation to occur in the relatives of mongols. The incidence of mongolism increases sharply as the age of the mother increases. The risk of a woman of twenty having a mongol child is only about 1 in 3,000. For a woman of forty, however, the risk is about 1 in 100, and for a woman of forty-five it may be as much as 1 in 50. The usually negative family history and this curious effect of mother's age did not suggest any of the usual forms of genetic determination. In favour of genetic determination, on the other hand, is the observation that while fraternal twins of mongols are seldom also mongols, the identical twins of mongols (that is twins derived from a single fertilized egg cell and so with the same genetic constitution) are always also mongols. A second piece of evidence for genetic determination is the six recorded instances, all recent, of mongol women having children. Three of these six children, surprisingly, were also mongols. This suggested that some kind of unusual mutation was the cause of mongolism and some years ago workers at University College, London, examined the chromosomes of a mongol child, but owing to the inadequate techniques then available found nothing definitely abnormal. Early in 1959, however, first in France and then independently in Edinburgh, the new techniques of chromosome counting were applied to mongols and it was found that the dozen or so patients examined all had 47 chromosomes. The extra chromosome was very probably a third member of the 21st or 22nd pair, which, together with the $Y$ chromosome, are the smallest. The possibility that it was an extra $Y$ chromosome was considered, but this was unlikely, since a female mongol would then have an $XXY$ genetic constitution, which is known to produce not mongolism, but Klinefelter's syndrome. The distinction was more clearly made when an imbecile in an English colony for mental defectives was recognized to have both mongolism and Klinefelter's syndrome. On examination, he was found to have 48 chromosomes, that is two extra, being trisomic both for the sex chromosomes, and for the 21st or 22nd pair.

*Translocation: a second mechanism for the production of chromosome abnormalities*

Recently an interesting variant of mongolism has been found which is important because it explains the rare instances where several members of a family are mongols. These are indistinguishable externally from other mongols, but they have 46, and not 47, chromosomes and have two instead of three of chromosome 21. Detailed examination of the other chromosomes shows that one member of either pair 15 or pair 22 is unusually long. There is good reason to suppose that this extra long chromosome has risen from an uneven exchange (called a 'translocation') of chromosome material between chromosome 15 (or in other instances chromosome 22) and chromosome 21, so that the long chromosome is almost all of 15 plus almost all of 21, conventionally written as 15/21. In effect, therefore, mongols are trisomic for chromosome 21, although the third 21 is contained in the unusual 15/21 chromosome. Study of the chromosomes of the parents of these mongols has shown that often a mother (it probably could be the father, though this has not yet been reported) has only 45 chromosomes, with only one 21 chromosome, but once again most of a second 21 attached to 15 to give the long 15/21 chromosome. These women have a nearly normal total chromosome complement and are themselves normally developed, mentally and physically, but they have a special liability to have mongol children of the type with 46 chromosomes (inclusive of the double chromosome). When they form ova they produce four types, one with a 15/21 and a normal 21 chromosome, one with a 15/21 chromosome and no 21 chromosome, one with a normal 15 and 21 chromosome, one with a normal 15 and no 21 chromosome. This is shown in Figure 67.

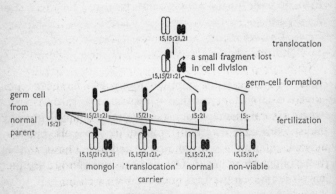

67. Chromosome 'translocation' resulting in familial mongolism

On fertilization by a normal sperm the first will give a mongol child; the second an apparently normal child but, like the mother, a carrier of the 15/21 chromosome; the third a normal individual; the fourth an individual who is truly monosomic for chromosome 21 and this will probably cause early death of the embryo. In families recently reported from The Hospital for Sick Children and Guy's Hospital, and from University College, London, the 15/21 chromosome has been traced back from mongol patients through their mothers to the maternal grandmothers.

*Further developments*

Chromosome studies in man are being pursued energetically in many centres. Trisomy of two other chromosomes is already established, each causing severe and characteristic abnormalities of development. Others may well cause intraembryonic death. As more powerful microscopy is used, it is probable that minor losses and reduplications of chromosomes will be recognized and related to specific human abnormalities. But it is already apparent that through mongolism an appreciable proportion of all mental defect, and that through Klinefelter's syndrome an appreciable proportion of all male sterility is caused by non-disjunction of chromosomes. Recently it has been shown that about a quarter of early abortions are due to chromosome abnormalities. Two of the commonest types found in early abortions are the *XO* genotype and triploidy, that is trisomy of all the chromosomes.

Little is yet known and intensive study is needed of the factors which are responsible for the development of chromosome abnormalities. Animal experiments have shown that irradiation can cause chromosome aberrations, including an increase in the total number of chromosomes.

# CHAPTER 11

# Some Diseases and Malformations due to Single Abnormal Mutant Genes

ONE can classify normal human variation into that which is mostly due to genetic difference, that which is mostly due to differing environmental experience, and that which is a combination of both genetic and environmental difference. In the same way one may classify malformations and disease processes.

A small proportion of all disease and malformation is largely genetically determined. This is particularly true of the conditions which are due to the chromosome abnormalities, discussed in the last chapter, and those due to mutant genes of large effect, dominant, recessive and sex-linked recessive, of which some examples are given in this Chapter. But for the reasons given in Chapters 8 and 9, nearly all the conditions due to mutant genes of large effect are rare disorders if they are at all serious. As will be seen in Chapter 12, the genetics of common disorders is nearly always complex and difficult to unravel.

## DOMINANT MUTANT GENES: SOME EXAMPLES OF CONDITIONS DUE TO SUCH GENES

### Achondroplasia

In most large circuses there are some dwarf clowns; these are usually very short, thick-set individuals with large square heads. The upper parts of their arms and legs are particularly short. Their intelligence and physical fitness, at any rate in those who survive infancy, is near normal. Their biological fitness is, however, very low; few have children and the affected women can only have children by Caesarean section. The essential abnormality is a failure of the change from gristle to bone at the growing ends of the long bones; but the exact nature of the alteration in the normal chemistry of the gristle and bone cells is not yet known.

A proportion of children born with this condition die very young and in some of these the condition may not be due to genetic factors. The family trees of those who survive suggest that the condition in them is due to one or more dominant genes. Since their biological fitness is low, most of them are born to normal parents. On the other hand, when they do have children, half their children on the average are affected in the same way. The families of two such patients known to the author are shown in Figure 68, and Plate 3 shows the affected mother and son in the first family.

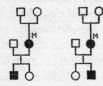

68. Two family trees
of patients with
achondroplasia

All four of the children of the two achondroplastic mothers were born by Caesarean section. If either of the two affected boys has children, the risk for each of these children of being affected is a half.

An interesting feature for the children affected by fresh mutations is that the father's age at their birth, rather more than the mother's, tends to be above the average age of fathers of new-born children. This may provide a clue to the cause of the mutation or mutations concerned. The production of sperm cells involves more cell divisions, and so more copying of the chromosomes, than the production of egg cells. This suggests that the mutation concerned is one that is especially likely to occur in the copying process.

There is little doubt that this particular dominant mutation has been recurring through history and probably prehistory; many statuettes of the ancient Egyptian god Bes represent him as achondroplastic.

The frequency of the condition appears to be about 1 in 40,000, and since those affected have a low fertility this indicates that the mutation rate of the gene-locus, or perhaps the summed mutation rates of the two or three gene-loci concerned, is of the same order.

## Familial polyposis of the large bowel

The abnormality in this condition consists of small growths (polyps) on the inner surface of the large bowel. They appear in childhood and cause little trouble till middle age. Some time in middle age, however, some of these growths develop into an invasive cancer, which spreads and if untreated kills the patient. The safest procedure once the condition is recognized is to remove nearly all the large bowel by operation before cancer develops. The patient is left with surprisingly little disability and has no longer any risk of dying of cancer. Fortunately, the children of affected individuals, who have a one in two risk of developing the condition, can be told whether they have the gene concerned or not by examination for the polyps, long before they themselves come to have children of their own. If they have no polyps they have little risk of transmitting the gene to their children. If they have developed polyps, then their children in turn have a one in two chance of developing the condition and of requiring the same operation.

The frequency of the condition is not known; but it is certainly rare, as one would expect with a condition due to a dominant gene which is likely to cause the death of some of those affected by it in early middle age. Dukes, the pathologist of one of the hospitals in London specializing in diseases of the large bowel, was recently able to report thirty-three families that had come to his notice, but these were drawn from a wide area. Three of the families he reported are shown in Figure 69. It will be seen that in the first two families (A and B), the mutant gene has disappeared in the third generation because those affected did not have children. In the third family (C) the present generation has been examined, those affected detected early and cancer prevented by removal of the large bowel.

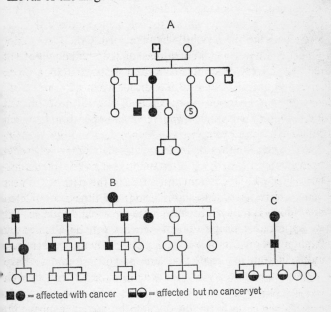

69. Pedigrees of familial polyposis of the large bowel recorded by Dukes

## Hereditary spherocytosis (acholuric jaundice)

The essential abnormality produced by the mutant gene responsible for this disease is that the red blood cells are more rounded than is normal and, associated with this, more fragile than normal. This can be shown in the laboratory by subjecting the cells to increasing dilutions of salt solution; cells from patients affected by this disease burst much sooner than cells from normal men and women. The exact nature of the chemical abnormality responsible for the swelling of the cells has not yet been found.

All patients with hereditary spherocytosis destroy their red cells more quickly than normal and so tend to have anaemia and low-grade jaundice; the jaundice is due to the breakdown products of the red pigment in the red cells. Some patients are very little handicapped. Others get periodic crises when for unknown reasons the breakdown of the red cells is very much increased and those affected become severely anaemic and very jaundiced. Most of the red cell destruction occurs in the spleen and the health of affected individuals can be much improved by an operation in which the spleen is removed.

When the families of patients with hereditary spherocytosis are investigated, it is often found that no relative is similarly affected. This is sometimes due to the patient's illness being the result of a fresh mutation; the fitness of affected individuals is reduced because some die in childhood so that an appreciable proportion of patients will be affected by fresh mutations. In other instances, while neither parent has any symptom of the disease, one parent is found to have spherocytosis and so has the gene like the patient, though less severely affected by it. Judging by symptoms, therefore, it is possible to have the disease skipping a generation, being transmitted, say, from grandparent to one or more grandchildren through an apparently normal parent.

The incidence of the disease in Europeans is estimated to be between 1 in 10,000 and 1 in 20,000. Since fitness is well above a half, this would fit with a not unreasonable mutation rate for a single gene-locus; but there are indications that there is more than one type of the disorder.

*Gout*

The symptoms of gout are due to the deposit of crystals of the sodium salt of uric acid in the tissues around joints. There are recurrent attacks of swelling and pain in one or more joints. As with hereditary spherocytosis the cause of the acute attacks is not known. The underlying abnormality, however, is in the body's metabolism of the base purine, the precursor of uric acid, such that the level of urates in the blood is unusually high at all times. The attacks of arthritis usually do not begin till the patient is middle-aged.

Family studies of gout suggest that a dominant mutant gene may be responsible but there are many skips in the pedigrees. Chemical studies, however, show that those who appeared to transmit gout without themselves being affected often had the unusually high levels of urate in the blood. In women the urate level in the blood is normally lower than in men, so that even when they possess the mutant gene for gout their blood urate levels though above normal are usually still insufficiently high to give attacks of gout. If the unusually high level of urate in the blood is taken as the effect of the gene there are few skips, and the family patterns fit those of a dominant gene, but would also fit multifactorial inheritance.

The incidence of gout in the population is rather less than 1 in 1,000. The proportion, however, of those who carry the gene responsible, but who are not affected by it, is probably about ten times greater. Since fitness will not be much reduced by gout these frequencies would fit a normally low mutation rate.

*Huntington's chorea*

This rare condition is perhaps the most striking of the diseases due to dominant genes which affect the brain. The abnormality is a degeneration of the nerve tissue in the brain, affecting some parts more than others. The two main symptoms are the development of continuous involuntary movements and progressive mental deterioration.

The first full description was given in 1872 by the American physician after whom the disease is named. He described cases in families in Long Island. Earlier affected members in these families had been known to his father, and to his grandfather who started medical practice there in 1797. Huntington was able to show that the mutant gene had been present in immigrants from Bures in Suffolk, who landed at Boston in 1630. In one case the line of descent could be traced unbroken through twelve generations to one of these immigrants. Some of those affected were accused in the Salem witch trials.

The disease may have an onset at any time from childhood to old age, but the majority are affected in early middle age. Obviously young adults who are the children of men or women affected with this condition are in an unenviable situation. They have a one in two chance of developing the condition by inheritance of the gene from their affected parent, while if they have children themselves and later develop the condition these children will be in the same difficult situation. Some method of detecting the presence of the gene before it causes overt disease would be a great boon to the 50 per cent or so of the individuals in these families who will not have received the gene. They cannot transmit it to their children and have no cause to fear their own future. The other 50 per cent would know for certain that there was a one in two risk for their children.

## RECESSIVE MUTANT GENES: TWO EXAMPLES OF CONDITIONS DUE TO SUCH GENES

### Fibrocystic disease of the pancreas

This is the most common of all diseases due to mutant genes of large effect in this country, other countries of northern

Europe, and North America. It probably affects about 1 child in 2,000. The essential abnormalities appear to be that the mucus secreted by the mucous glands in the digestive and respiratory tracts is abnormally viscid, and the sweat glands produce sweat which has an unusually high content of salt. The main effects of this disease are due to the viscid mucous secretion. The duct of the pancreatic gland which produces some of the main digestive ferments tends to become blocked, so that digestion of fats and protein foodstuffs is incomplete. The smaller air ducts in the lungs tend to become blocked and then infection develops in the blocked ducts. In the past no patients have been known to survive into adult life; but now patients are being increasingly successfully treated with animal pancreatic extract to overcome the digestive disturbance, and with drugs such as penicillin to control the lung infection. The loss of salt in the sweat causes no trouble in this country, but may lead to heat exhaustion in a hot climate.

It is very probable that a recessive mutant gene is responsible for this disease. It is established that the risk to brothers and sisters of patients of being affected also is close to one in four, while other relatives are rarely affected. No increase in first cousin marriages has yet been shown among the parents of patients. This, however, is understandable as the disease is so common. The carrier frequency in the population, assuming that the frequency of homozygotes is 1 in 2,000, will be between one in twenty and one in twenty-five, so that the risk of a man heterozygous for the gene marrying another carrier is only increased three- or four-fold if he marries a first cousin.

A frequency of 1 child in 2,000 affected is too high to be maintained simply by fresh mutation and suggests that carriers must have some selective advantages over those homozygous for the normal gene. There are no indications of the nature of this advantage. It has also not proved possible to detect the carriers reliably, though there are indications that some of them may have a rather more concentrated sweat than normals.

## Phenylketonuria

This disease, to which reference has been made several times in earlier chapters because the nature of the abnormality is unusually well understood, affects about 1 child in 40,000 in this country, northern Europe, and North America. The essential lack is in the ability to change the aminoacid phenylalanine to tyrosine. One of the standard tests often made in hospital is the addition of ferric chloride to a specimen of the patient's urine. Ferric chloride gives a green compound with one of the derivatives of phenylalanine which appears in the urine of patients with phenylketonuria. Once this reaction had been discovered it was simple to test the urine of patients in hospitals for severely mentally handicapped children, and it was found that about 1 in 100 of the patients in these hospitals were suffering from phenylketonuria. It then became clear that about one in four of the brothers and sisters of patients were similarly affected and that some of the affected children were the offspring of a cousin marriage. Further experience has shown that while most patients with this condition are severely mentally defective, a few have intelligence quotients well above the defective level.

Determined attempts are now being made in several centres to treat these children on diets from which all phenylalanine has been removed, on the principle that the mental defect is not an essential part of the disease but due to poisonous by-products of phenylalanine. There are indications that this treatment may be partially successful provided that treatment is started very early in life.

In recent years, too, great advances have been made in detecting the carriers. The first method was by giving the suspected carriers a large dose of phenylalanine and showing that it was not cleared as quickly from their blood as in normals. More recently, it has been found that a single test of the level in the blood before breakfast will distinguish carriers from normals in most instances.

## SEX-LINKED RECESSIVE MUTANT GENES: EXAMPLES OF CONDITIONS CAUSED IN THIS WAY

### Diabetes insipidus of renal origin

Diabetes insipidus or 'water' diabetes, is the condition in which large amounts of urine are excreted by the kidney, due to a failure of the kidney to concentrate urine. This concentration normally occurs in the tubules of the kidney under the influence of a hormone secreted by the posterior part of the pituitary gland. The amount of this hormone secretion and of the degree of concentration of urine is determined by the amount of water in the body, When a man drinks more water than he needs the secretion of hormone falls and he gets rid of water by passing a dilute urine; when he is short of water the hormone secretion rises so that he keeps what water he has by excreting a concentrated urine.

Diabetes insipidus is of two types. In the first type it is the secretion of posterior pituitary hormone which is lacking. These patients can be treated with posterior pituitary extract from animals. In the second type there is no abnormality in posterior pituitary secretion, but the tubules fail to concentrate the urine even when large amounts of posterior pituitary hormone are present. Two distinct types of mutant gene, one dominant and one sex-linked recessive, which cause the first type are known. The second type is more serious, In this there is no way of increasing the concentrating capacity of the kidney and the only way that the kidneys can excrete the waste products of metabolism is by excreting large quantities of water at the same time. This is only possible if the affected individuals are drinking large amounts of water. If the condition is not suspected affected children do not, in fact, get enough water, the waste products of metabolism accumulate in their blood and tissues, and they may die young or become mentally defective. Even if the condition is recognized it may be necessary in infancy to keep them on a low food intake, especially of foods containing salts and nitrogen compounds, so that the amount of waste products to be excreted is limited.

The condition is probably due in most instances to a sex-linked recessive mutant gene. The gene is, however, not

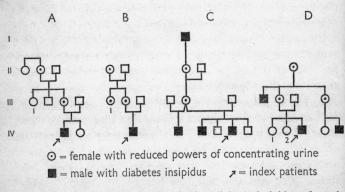

⊙ = female with reduced powers of concentrating urine

■ = male with diabetes insipidus   ↗ = index patients

70. Family trees of four patients having diabetes insipidus of renal origin

totally recessive, so that in many instances it is possible to recognize the heterozygous female carriers of the disease. This is valuable in a disease where early treatment may be needed to prevent death or mental defect. Carrier women usually have no overt abnormality, except that as children they may have had to keep water by their beds to drink in the night. If, however, their ability to concentrate urine is tested by asking them to drink nothing for twelve hours, it is usually found to be well below that of normal individuals, though better than that of the affected sons and brothers. The families of four patients with this condition known to the author are shown in Figure 70. The concentration tests show that the young woman III, 1 and the girl IV, 2 in pedigree A and the girls IV, 1 and 2 in pedigree D are not carriers, but the young woman III, 1 in pedigree B is almost certainly a carrier.

## Duchenne type muscular dystrophy

The term 'muscular dystrophy' is used to describe a group of diseases in which there is progressive weakness and wasting of the muscles, the abnormality arising in the muscles themselves and not in the nervous system. Dominant and recessive forms are known, but the type most commonly seen in children, often called Duchenne type, is sex-linked. Unfortunately no treatment is yet available and the nature of the basic muscle defect is unknown.

The lack of any effective treatment makes it all the more important to be able to pick out the carrier women in families in which the disease has occurred, and equally to recognize those who do not carry the gene and so cannot have effected sons. Affected boys have very high levels of creatine kinase in their blood plasma, due to leakage of this enzyme from the dystrophic muscles, into the blood. Recently it has been shown that the majority of women who carry the sex-linked gene concerned may be recognised by their having a level of creatine kinase in the blood plasma much lower than that found in the affected boys, but higher than that found in women who do not carry the gene.

# CHAPTER 12

# Some Common Illnesses for which there is Genetic Predisposition

THE conditions chosen to illustrate the part played by genetic factors in common illnesses are diabetes mellitus or 'sugar diabetes', gastric and duodenal ulcer, rheumatic fever, mental retardations, the two main types of insanity, and epilepsy. For reasons mentioned earlier, it is not to be expected that common illnesses will have a simple genetic determination. In most instances all that can be shown at the moment is that genetic factors probably play some part in causing the disease.

But because the illnesses chosen are common most people will have a relative who suffers from one of these diseases and readers should not let this cause them anxiety for their own health or that of their children. The conditions where there is a high risk of hereditary transmission are nearly all of the type described in Chapter 10 due to a single mutant gene of large effect. Even here the reader should not apply the risks quoted to his own case without consulting his family doctor, who will if necessary arrange for expert advice.

## Diabetes mellitus

Diabetes mellitus or 'sugar' diabetes resembles diabetes insipidus (see page 213), in that large amounts of urine are passed. The essential abnormality here, however, is a failure of the body's use of glucose sugar; so that the level of glucose in the blood is high and this spills over into the urine. The sugar in the urine prevents concentration of the urine so that a great deal is passed. There are different degrees of the disorder. The milder degrees, commoner in older people, may often be treated merely by restricting the glucose-forming constituents of the diet, sugars and starch. In the severer forms, commoner in younger people, the disease needs to be controlled by daily or twice daily injections of insulin. Insulin is the hormone from the pancreas which favours the utilization of glucose by the muscles.

Family studies show a definite family concentration of the disease. A number of surveys have been made in America, England, Russia, and Switzerland and, most recently, Denmark. No exact figures are available for the risk to the members of the general population of developing diabetes at some time in their lives, but it is probably between 1 and 2 per cent in the countries mentioned. Much the greater part of this risk occurs after the age of forty, though the onset may be much earlier and even occur in infancy. The risks to the near relatives of diabetics is certainly higher than this. In identical twins it is of the order of 50 per cent and would be higher than this if these co-twins were followed to the end of their lives. Among fraternal twins the risk is notably lower, about 10 per cent. In non-twin brothers and sisters the proportion found affected is about 5 per cent, and the risk is probably about 15 per cent if allowance is made for those who are yet to develop the disease. This risk is about doubled if one of the parents is also a diabetic. The proportion of parents affected is much the same as that for brothers and sisters, and probably lower if allowance is made for their greater age. No satisfactory information is yet available for the risks to the children of diabetics, but it may well prove to be much the same as for parents.

It seems very likely then, that genetic factors are important in causing diabetes, but no very reliable conclusions may yet be drawn on the mechanism of the inheritance of the illness. The finding that half the identical co-twins of diabetics are unaffected shows that the genetic predisposition does not always take effect. There are indications that there may be more than one type of genetic predisposition since patients in the same family tend, in general, to resemble each other for the age at which they develop their diabetes, though there are plenty of exceptions. In one series of patients who were attending a London hospital, and were investigated by Harris, there were an unusual number of patients who were the offspring of cousin marriages among those with an early onset of diabetes; but not among those with a late onset of the illness.

It would be useful in treatment and even prevention if among young relatives of patients with diabetes, those who were going to develop the disease could be recognized early. There is little doubt that a pre-diabetic state exists; for example, diabetic women have unusually heavy babies, and this is true also of babies born before the mother develops the illness. There are indications that early recognition may be possible, but no method is yet reliable.

## Gastric and duodenal ulcer

Two of the commonest diseases are ulcers of the stomach and of the first part of the small intestine leading from the stomach known as the duodenum. The causes of the two conditions are not known, but there are indications that environmental factors such as diet and occupation play a part. It also seems probable, however, that there is a genetic predisposition. In one recent study by Doll and Buch in northwest London it was found that the fathers, mothers, brothers, and sisters of patients with gastric and duodenal ulcers had such ulcers themselves more than twice as often as the members of the general population in the same area. For example, of the brothers over thirty-five years of age, fifty-four were found affected when only twenty-three would have been expected. It was not always possible to distinguish between the two types of ulcer in this investigation, but where it was possible, the type tended to be the same in the patient and his affected relation.

While it is possible that common family environment might account for this increased risk to relatives, it is unlikely. The problem could be solved by studies of the twins of patients and comparing the proportion of identical and fraternal twins also affected. The best twin study so far comes from the big Danish twin study, now being undertaken, of all twins born between 1870 and 1910. The results to date are that twelve of twenty-nine identical co-twins and ten of forty-six fraternal co-twins (of the same sex) are also affected. While the series is still too small to exclude chance as a cause of the differences between the two types of twins, the results favour genetic predisposition of the conditions.

The genetic predisposition here is likely to be multifactorial. A most interesting recent discovery is that, as mentioned in Chapter 3, the genes determining the ABO blood groups, and the genes which determine whether the mucus in saliva and other bodily secretions have ABO group specific antigens, influence the risk of developing duodenal ulcer. The tendency for near relatives to have the same ABO blood group and resemble each other for the secretor factor would, however, account for only about five per cent of the increased risk to near relatives of duodenal ulcer. Other genes must also be concerned.

*Rheumatic fever*

A number of children react to an infection of their throats by streptococcal bacteria by developing an illness known as rheumatic fever. They develop fever, pain, and inflammation in several joints, and in many instances inflammation of the valves of the heart as well. The fever and the joint inflammation settle and leave no after-effects, but the inflammation of the valves of the heart may lead to scarring of these valves and impairment of their function. This is particularly likely to happen where the child has had several attacks of rheumatic fever, and rheumatic fever is the commonest cause of severe heart disease in young adults. In all, about 2 per cent of children in temperate climates develop rheumatic fever.

However, almost all children develop streptococcal infections of their throats and there must be additional factors which determine whether the infection leads to rheumatic fever. Some of the additional factors are environmental and associated with living conditions. Rheumatic fever is more common in children in the lower socio-economic classes. For example, when rheumatic fever was included among the diseases to be notified to the Medical Officer of Health in Sheffield in 1947, it was found to occur proportionately three times more often among the children of men who were unskilled labourers than among the children of men in professional and managerial occupations. But this environmental influence does not seem enough to explain the concentration of rheumatic fever that is found within families. The first degree relatives of patients with the illness are five to ten times as likely to have had the illness as are members of the general population. If neither parent has had the disease the risk of the brothers and sisters of patients is about one in ten. The risk to the children of patients is also found to be about one in ten, and both these findings underestimate the true risk since some of these relatives may develop the disease later. An additional finding which is difficult to explain on purely environmental grounds is that where the patients had a parent who was also affected the risk to brothers and sisters is doubled. In the few families known where both parents were affected the majority of the children in the family developed the disease. There are, as yet, no large series of twins where one has rheumatic fever, but there are strong indications that identical co-twins of patients are more often affected than are fraternal co-twins. In the Danish series, 6 of 35 identical pairs and 10 of 145 fraternal pairs are concordant.

Rheumatic fever, therefore, provides an instance of a disease where the immediate cause is environmental (infection by a bacillus) and where additional environmental factors related to living conditions play a part. But genetic predisposition is also important in determining whether a child reacts to the infection by developing rheumatic fever.

*Inheritance of mental defect*

Over one-third of all hospital beds in this country are occupied by men, women, and children with mental defect or mental illness. These two conditions are quite distinct. Mental defect is a defective capacity for thought. In mental illness thought is disordered and out of touch with reality, but within the limits of the disorder the patient may be highly intelligent. Mental defect is usually present from birth and the more severe forms can be recognized as early as six months of age. There are, however, forms which develop later in childhood and some which develop in adult life. The onset of mental illness of the type commonly spoken of as insanity is nearly always in adult life, though there are occasionally young children who show a mental illness in many ways resembling one of the adult forms of insanity, schizophrenia. Contrary to common belief there is no connexion between insanity and mental deficiency.

The milder forms of mental defect are best regarded as part of the normal variation of intelligence. The defect is due to the same kind of factors as those which determine the differences between dull, average, and bright individuals. These factors are in part genetic and in part environmental. About 1 child of school-age in 50 is affected with a mild degree of mental defect. The severer forms of mental defect are mostly due to definite disorder or malformation of the brain and about 1 school-age child in 300 is affected with this degree of defect. The proportion at birth with severe defect is perhaps twice as high, since many of the mentally handicapped children are delicate and die in infancy or early childhood.

There is overlap in intelligence level between the two groups and it is not always easy to assign a child with an I.Q. about 50 to the correct group. Children whose mental handicap is certainly due to a disease process, such as phenylketonuria, brain damage from rhesus incompatibility, or mongolism, may occasionally have an I.Q. above 50 while in some children with an I.Q. of about 40 there is no apparent evidence of any disease or malformation even on post-mortem examination. Nevertheless, the distinction between 'normal' and 'pathological' forms is useful and the more severe the mental defect the more probable it is that the cause is malformation or disease.

The near relatives of patients with the milder degrees of mental defect show the usual regression towards the mean of the population. They have intelligence distributed round a level well below the average, but well above that of the defective patients. This fits with the theory that these patients are part of the normal variation of intelligence, the counterparts at the bottom end of the scale (of intelligence) of highly intelligent individuals at the top end.

The near relatives of patients with severe mental defect show a very different pattern. They fall into two groups: a large majority whose distribution of intelligence is close to that of the general population, and a small minority who are as handicapped as the patient themselves. Where the defect of intelligence in the patients is due to some accidental injury to the brain, before or after birth, it is understandable that relatives should be normal. Where the defect of intelligence is due to mutant genes of large effect, relatives will either be normal or will have the same genetic predisposition and so tend to be affected in the same way as the patient. Not all the genetically determined types of severe mental defect can be distinguished. It is found, for example, that among the parents of children with severe defect of non-specific type, there are more cousin marriages than in the population at large, suggesting that some of these children are affected by as yet unrecognized recessive genes. It is probably largely because of the existence of these unrecognized recessive types of defect, that the risk of mental deficiency in later brothers and sisters of children with non-specific severe mental defect is above the random risk.

Where there are any specific features accompanying the mental defect, however, there is usually little difficulty in recognizing the types of defect due to recessive inheritance, by the usual criteria; that is, the one in four risk to brothers and sisters of being affected in the same way, and the increase in cousin marriages in the parents. With severe mental defect due to dominant mutant genes, the recognition of the mode of inheritance may not be easy, since it is very rare for men and women with this degree of mental defect to have children. This was also true of severe mental defect due to chromosome abnormalities until the new methods of observing chromosomes were developed.

## Mental illness

It is a popular belief that insanity is strongly inherited. This is only partly correct. It is true that, in contrast to most disturbances of organs other than the brain, insanity can seldom be attributed to some known environmental cause, such as a vitamin deficiency, a poison, infection, or severe mental stress. There is also good evidence that genetic predisposition is often important in determining whether or not a man or woman becomes insane. But additional environmental factors must also be important. Mental illness is common. About 1 individual in 30 at some time or other in his life suffers from mental illness, and so any genetic predisposition for such illness must be widespread in the population. Because of this generally high risk of developing mental illness, even if there were no genetic predisposition one would often find that a patient has at least one relative who also has a history of mental illness. In order to prove that genetic factors play a part it must be shown that near relatives of the mentally ill are more often also mentally ill than are members of the general population, and that this cannot be explained by common environment. Both twin studies and the family studies, however, indicate that there really is often a genetic predisposition and that on the whole this predisposition is specific. One type of mental illness only tends to occur within one particular family.

## Types of mental illness

The classification of mental illness is difficult and not fully agreed, but two main groups are recognized, schizophrenia and manic-depressive insanity. Something like two-thirds of mentally ill patients can be assigned to one or the other group. There are those individuals whose illness shows features of both types, and here experts may differ on the correct assignment. There are also varieties of illness which do not belong to either group. At the moment, neither chemical investigations in life nor pathological investigations after death are of much help in the classification.

Manic-depressive illness is typically characterized by changes in mood, which occur in cycles. In the manic phases the patient is abnormally active mentally and physically, and his mood is one of elation. In the depressive phases, the mood, as the name suggests, is one of severe depression and physical and mental activity are much reduced. Swings of mood of a lesser degree are a common experience, but in manic-depressive insanity they are more severe, and such that the patient may lose touch with reality. Often only at the peaks of the illness does the patient need admission to hospital, and many patients need admission to hospital on only a single occasion. In schizophrenic illness the mood is typically one of withdrawal and indifference and the thought disorders are more bizarre. The illness is usually more prolonged, so that while the proportion of the population who develop schizophrenia is no higher than that of those who develop depressive insanity, the number of patients in mental hospitals with schizophrenia is always much higher than the number with manic-depressive insanity.

## Twin studies in mental illness

A number of twin studies have been made for both types of mental illness in Germany, America, and in this country. They agree in showing that the risk of identical co-twins of patients also being affected with mental illness is significantly higher than the risk for like-sex fraternal co-twins. They agree in the finding that the risk among like-sex fraternal co-twins is of the same order as the risk to non-twin brothers and sisters of the patients, and notably higher than the risk in the general population. Further, they show that where the co-twin is also affected he has a type of mental illness which is of the same general type as that of the patient.

The manic-depressive series are on a rather small scale and the precautions needed in getting an unbiased sample of twins were probably not always fully observed, but they show from 50 to 70 per cent of the identical co-twins also affected and 20 to 25 per cent of like-sex fraternal co-twins also affected. Unfortunately, no series is yet available for manic-depressive psychosis where the twins had been brought up apart. For schizophrenia the twin studies are considerably larger, since more patients are available and here the English, German, and American series agree in showing 60 to 80 per cent of identical co-twins also affected in contrast to 10 to 15 per cent of like-sex fraternal co-twins. Kallmann of the New York State Psychiatric Service has a series of identical co-twins of patients with schizophrenia, where the twins have been reared apart. He has not published full details of these, but he has indicated that the proportion of the co-twins also affected is almost as high as when they are reared together. If these findings on twins reared apart are confirmed they will be evidence of the major importance of the genetic constitution in determining schizophrenia.

## Family studies of manic-depressive insanity

Turning to family studies, it is found that the proportion of first degree relatives of manic-depressive patients who are also affected with manic-depressive insanity is of much the same order, though a little less than the proportion of like-sex fraternal twins. The proportion of relatives who have schizophrenia is no higher than that in the general population. One of the best family studies was carried out by Stenstedt in Sweden who took as his starting-point all instances of manic-depressive psychosis from two areas of Sweden from 1919 to 1948. He found that of the brothers and sisters 7 per cent were certainly affected and another 7 per cent possibly affected. For parents the proportions were 5 per cent and 7·5 per cent, for children 11 per cent and 17 per cent. The figure for children approaches the risk for the like-sex fraternal twins. The actual manifestation of the illness varied in different members of the same family. The family study suggested that patients with many attacks and patients with few attacks, patients with mainly manic symptoms and patients with mainly depressive symptoms, patients with an early onset and those with a late onset of the illness, all had varieties of essentially the same disorder, since all these varieties might occur within a single family.

On the other hand Stenstedt found that involutional psychosis, a type of insanity that occurs particularly in women past the menopause, did not occur in these families and so was genetically distinct. The fact that the proportion of identical co-twins also affected is well below 100 per cent indicates that environmental factors must play a part in deciding whether any genetic predisposition to manic-depressive psychosis takes effect or not. Looking for such factors in the childhood environment of his patients, Stenstedt divided them into two groups: those coming from a disturbed home, for example with parents divorced or separated; and those with no such unfavourable experience. He found that this had a notable effect on the proportion of brothers and sisters of the patients who were also affected. For those with an unfavourable home background the risk, including probable but not certain cases, was 30 per cent, while for the remainder it was 10 per cent. This suggests that a psychologically unfavourable early environment of this kind helps to make manifest any genetic predisposition to develop manic-depressive insanity. Such an unfavourable home background is not, of course, in itself, sufficient to cause the illness, since the great majority of those who come from such homes either develop no mental illness or only neurosis and not insanity.

## Family studies of schizophrenic insanity

Family studies have also been made for schizophrenic illness and these have shown that the varieties of schizophrenia have a common genetic origin since they tend to occur with above average frequency within the same family. Family studies provided, for example, good confirmation that paranoia, a form of insanity in which there are delusions of persecution in an otherwise intact personality, was part of the schizophrenia group. The risks to brothers and sisters of patients with schizophrenia is of the order of 10 per cent and the risk to children is similar. Here again environmental factors must also play a part, though no one has yet shown how the risk is modified by environment in the way that Stenstedt has shown for manic-depressive insanity.

The exact genetic mechanisms underlying manic-depressive insanity and schizophrenia are not known and are probably complex. There is an indication that recessive genes may be concerned in a proportion of schizophrenic illness from the finding that where insane patients have parents who are first cousins, the illness is unduly often of the schizophrenic type. The fertility of manic-depressives is not much reduced, and so a frequency of the illness in the population as high as 1 per cent is not difficult to explain. With schizophrenia however, fertility is much reduced, because of its earlier on-set and usually more prolonged course, and it is not easy to see how the frequency of the genetic factors concerned is maintained in the population. To make a complete genetic analysis of insanity it will probably be necessary to wait until the underlying errors of the body's metabolism are better understood. Some chemical abnormalities are already known in patients during the active phases of their illness, but it is not clear yet whether they are fundamental to the illness or merely a by-product. None of those yet known are present when the patient has recovered, and so they are not likely to be useful in picking out relations of patients who have the same genetic predisposition, but have never developed mental illness.

*Epilepsy*

There has long been a popular belief that epilepsy is strongly inherited, but this is largely mistaken. In Sweden it was until recently illegal for an epileptic to marry, unless first sterilized, though the law was little observed. Epileptic attacks may be a symptom of underlying disease of various types, and here the inheritance will be that of the underlying disease. A few of these diseases are due to gene mutations of large effect, but they are rare. One example is a condition known as tuberose sclerosis. This is due to a dominant mutant gene and all those who have the gene have small growths of the deeper layer of the skin on the nose and surrounding parts of the cheek. These skin growths are disfiguring but no danger to health. Some patients with this disease may also have growths in the heart, kidney, or brain. In the two former sites the growths usually cause no symptoms, but the growths in the brain lead to mental defect and severe epileptic fits. In contrast, where epilepsy is consequent on brain damage following, for example, an attack of tuberculous meningitis, there is no increased tendency for relatives to be affected.

## Epilepsy with no known cause

In most instances, however, there is no apparent underlying cause of the epilepsy. This idiopathic epilepsy shows a definite concentration within families, but seldom gives patterns suggestive of single gene determination. The proportion of identical co-twins of children with idiopathic epilepsy also affected is certainly high (in one American study it was 80 per cent) but there may have been some bias in the way that the twins came to notice in this series. In the same series the risk for fraternal co-twins was only about 20 per cent. Family studies of children with idiopathic epilepsy show a risk for first degree relatives of about 4 per cent, compared with a risk for the general population, by the same standards, of between 1 and 2 per cent.

Within families too, the type of epilepsy tends to be the same. If the patient has epilepsy which responds well to treatment and clears up later in childhood, then the epilepsy in affected relatives usually behaves in the same way. Children who have fits only when they have a fever also fall into this group. If the epilepsy in the patient does not clear up, then, too, epilepsy in relatives tends to be of the same kind. It would appear therefore, that there are at least two types of epilepsy each with a genetic predisposition. A puzzling group have been the patients who have a severe epileptic attack early in childhood, which continues to death. Family studies show that the relatives of children with this type of epilepsy give the family pattern of children with ordinary persistent epilepsy, which is resistant to treatment.

One of the most useful aids in investigation of patients with epilepsy is an electrical recording of the brain's activity. These recordings are usually much alike in identical twins. It has been found that where an epileptic child has an unaffected identical co-twin, it is not uncommon for this co-twin to have an electrical recording similar to that which is found in epilepsy. Similarly, it has been found both in America and Denmark that among the unaffected relatives of patients with epilepsy, there are an undue number who have abnormal recordings. It was hoped, therefore, that these abnormal recordings might be indicative of a genetic predisposition to epilepsy. Unfortunately, this can only be partly true. In many instances where epilepsy has very probably been transmitted to a patient from an unaffected relative through an unaffected carrier, this carrier has a normal electrical recording.

# CHAPTER 13

## Congenital Deformities

*Congenital malformations and public health*

CONGENITAL malformations, that is malformations present at birth, are becoming increasingly important for child health. They are not becoming more common; but most other causes of ill-health in childhood are being successfully treated, even prevented, so congenital malformations are relatively more important. In 1902, for example, the number of live-born children dying in the first year of life in England and Wales was 133 per 1,000. In 1960 it was only 22 per 1,000. Every year, however, the proportion certified as dying from congenital malformations is much the same, about $4\frac{1}{2}$ per 1,000. In 1902 these malformations were making only a small contribution – about one-thirtieth – to the total death rate. In 1960 they contributed about one-fifth. Since a congenital malformation, though an important contributory cause, is not always mentioned on the death certificate, it is estimated that now such malformations are the main cause of death of 1 child in 4 dying in the first year of life. In addition to the malformations severe enough to cause early death there are a larger number which, to a greater or lesser degree, handicap the child. Something like 1 child in 50 live born, that is about 20 per 1,000, have a severe or moderately severe physical malformation. The most common malformations are those of the central nervous system and of the heart, though malformations of the skeleton are also common.

*Causes of congenital malformations*

The causes of congenital malformations are largely unknown. One common belief is that upsets, physical and emotional, of the mother in pregnancy may cause malformation; this is incorrect. Equally prevalent is the view that any condition present at birth must be inherited; this is also incorrect. In fact, not much is known about the causes of congenital malformations. There are indications, as we shall show, that genetic predisposition is important for the development of many common malformations. But it is also clear that only a minority of the children with such genetic predispositions are affected; environmental factors, mostly as yet unknown, must also play a part.

Experiments with animals, so rewarding in most fields of medicine, have not contributed much directly to our understanding of human congenital malformations. It is possible to produce malformed offspring by subjecting female rats or mice to temporary and relatively minor upsets early in pregnancy. While severe vitamin deficiencies in the pregnant female will result in death of the foetus, milder deficiencies or excesses may result in surviving malformed offspring. There is no clear evidence at the moment, however, that such factors are a cause of malformations in humans, or cause the malformations that occur naturally in wild and domestic animals. These animal experiments, however, have been valuable in showing that environmental influences which are hardly enough to disturb the mother, may damage the foetus she is carrying. Also they have been valuable in suggesting that often it is not the type of the environmental influence that is important in determining the kind of malformation, but the precise moment in the development of the embryo at which the influence takes effect. The few days in which the development of a particular organ is proceeding most rapidly are probably those in which a noxious influence is most likely to cause a malformation.

*Infection in pregnancy and malformation*

The one known recurrent environmental cause of malformation in humans is the virus infection German measles.
This discovery was made by an Australian eye specialist in
1942; he noted that many of the young children he was seeing
with congenital cataract, an opacity of the lens of the eye,
had been born to mothers affected by German measles in the
early months of pregnancy. It was soon established that the
malformations which were most often caused in this way
were cataract, malformations of the heart, and deafness. To
produce the malformations the mother's attack of German
measles needed to be in the first three months of the pregnancy, or in the first four months in the case of partial deafness. This was to be expected since this is the period when
tissues are forming. The risk of major malformation after
infection in the first three months was found, in a survey
carried out over all England, Wales, and Scotland between
1950 and 1952, to be about one in six, and there was an
additional risk of about one in eight of incomplete deafness.
This risk, however, may vary with different epidemics. A
survey in France gave a higher risk, and another in Sweden
a lower risk.

Once this effect of German measles had been found, it was
natural to look for evidence that other virus infections such
as ordinary measles, mumps, infantile paralysis, and influ-
enza might cause congenital malformations. No convincing
evidence has, as yet, been found of any similar effect of these
other infections. German measles in pregnancy is a rare
event and only a very small proportion of all congenital malformations can normally be accounted for in this way. The
drug thalidomide given early in pregnancy in 1960 and 1961
resulted in the birth of many skeletally malformed children,
before this unexpected danger was recognized.

When one studies the more common specific types of malformation it is usual to find that the causation is complex;

that both genetic predisposition and environmental factors, whose nature is not yet precisely worked out, are playing a part. A short account is given in the following pages of what is known of the causes of four common malformations; harelip (with or without lateral cleft palate) and congenital deafness, both of which are present at birth; pyloric stenosis, which may be present at birth or at any rate in the first few days of life; and congenital dislocation of the hip, which may be present at birth but probably does not develop until the first few months of life.

## Harelip and lateral cleft palate

Cleft palate occurs in two forms: one in which the cleft is central and there is no harelip, and one in which the cleft is to one side and there is always also a harelip on the side of the cleft. Sometimes the latter type of cleft occurs on both sides and then there is also a harelip on both sides. Family studies showed that the two forms were quite distinct, but that harelip without any cleft of the palate occurred in the families of patients with harelip and lateral cleft palate. It followed that harelip with or without an associated lateral cleft palate was genetically distinct from central cleft palate.

Large scale family studies have now been made for patients with harelip with or without lateral cleft palate, particularly in Denmark. The proportion of live-born babies with the malformation is about 1 in 1,000 in England and probably also in most north-European countries, but the proportion is nearly twice higher in boys than in girls. Near relatives of patients with the malformation have a considerably increased risk of being affected. For brothers and sisters, provided neither parent is also affected, the risk of having the malformation is about 1 in 30. Where a parent is also affected the risk to brothers and sisters is increased, perhaps to more than 1 in 10. The risk to children of patients with the malformation has recently been shown to be very similar to that to brothers and sisters, about 1 in 30. If, however, a patient does have an effected child the risk for a later brother or sister of the affected child rises to about 1 in 10. For aunts and uncles the risks are about 1 per cent and for first cousins only about 1 in 300. When a relative is affected the degree of the malformation is unrelated to that in the patient. For example, a patient with a harelip and cleft palate on both sides may have a brother with a simple one-sided harelip.

These risks are much less than for conditions simply determined by single mutant genes of large effect, dominant, recessive, or sex-linked recessive, such as those described in Chapter 11. On the other hand, for the near relatives they are much higher than the general risk in the population, and as one moves further away from the patient to aunts and uncles and cousins, the risk falls progressively towards the low risk in the general population.

Numerous genetic theories can be put forward to explain risks of this kind. They would be compatable, for example, with entirely genetic determination by several genes. Such complete genetic determination, however, is ruled out by studies of twins. No large-scale twin study has yet been made, but putting together those as yet available, of twelve identical co-twins three were also affected. This indicates that whatever the genetic predisposition, only a minority, perhaps only a quarter of those who have the predisposition, are actually affected. For fraternal co-twins the proportion affected was three in fifty-six, much the same as for non-twin brothers and sisters.

If one applies the evidence from identical twins, that the majority of individuals with the genetic predisposition are not affected, to the family risks, and assumes that for every relative affected there are about three with the genetic pre-disposition for the malformation but unaffected, the pattern becomes very close to that which could be given by multifactorial inheritance. The concept is, that an underlying multifactorial genetic predisposition gives a normal distribution similar to that discussed in Chapter 6 for height. Further, it is assumed that the embryos at risk of malformation are those beyond a threshold, equivalent to, say, those over seventy-five inches tall, such that about three in a thousand embryos are at risk and about one in a thousand actually have a harelip malformation, depending on whether the additional environmental factors come into play.

The expected risk to relatives on this hypothesis can be worked out. Brothers and sisters, sons and daughters of patients share, on average, half their genes in common with the index patients. The distribution of the multifactorial genotype will have the form of a normal curve, similar to, if a little narrower than, that of the general population. This substantial shift of the curve will bring 30 to 40 times as many of these near relatives beyond the threshold, and so at risk of harelip malformation, as in the general population. On the other hand, first cousins, sharing only 1 in 8 of their genes with the patients, will have a distribution about seven-eighths of the way back towards the population average, and only two or three times as many as in the general population will be at risk. Nothing however, is yet known of the environmental factors or the nature of the multifactorial predisposition.

## Pyloric stenosis

This genetically interesting condition is usually included among the congenital malformations, though it is not certain that this is correct. There is doubt whether it is present at birth, though it has been found to be present as early as the third day of life, and seldom develops after the first few months of life.

The essential abnormality appears to be overdevelopment of the muscle at the lower end of the stomach. The function of this muscle is to contract and hold food in the stomach while the first stage of the digestion of food takes place, then

o relax and let the partly digested food into the small intes-
ine. The effect of overdevelopment of the muscle is to predispose to an obstruction of the exit of food from the
stomach, which causes the baby to vomit, at first part and
later almost all of its food. By the end of about the fourth
month of life the effects of the condition have passed off, but
if untreated the baby may well die before the age of four
months from under-nutrition and infection of the intestines
or lungs. An effective operation which is nearly always completely successful in relieving this condition was discovered
in Germany in 1912 and consists simply in cutting through
the muscle on one side. There are normally no after-effects
of the condition. Medicinal treatments, though at the moment less reliable, are also being developed.

The proportion of children affected is about 1 live-born
child in 330 in north-west Europe. The condition is five times
commoner in boys than in girls, so the frequency is about
1 in 1,000 girls and 1 in 200 boys. The reason for this sex
difference is not yet certain.

It was early noticed that brothers and sisters of affected
children are not uncommonly also affected. In one large
family investigation from Birmingham it was found that
about 1 brother in 16 was also affected and about 1 in
54 sisters, a risk for both sexes combined of about 1 in 25.
For each sex the risk was nearly 12 times greater than that
in the general population. A more recent London survey con-
firms this, but also indicates that the risk is higher to the
brothers and sisters of affected girls than of affected boys.
Until recently it was rare to find a parent affected and this is
understandable, since it would seem that the proportion of
affected individuals who survived before 1920 was small.
Now however, some affected parents have had affected children. In one series of patients treated between 1948 and 1950
at a London hospital, it was found that about 1 in 50 mothers and 1 in 200 fathers were also affected. The series was too

small for these figures to be reliable, but it is interesting that
the usual rate of 4 male to 1 female is reversed in these
affected parents. Similarly, information on the risks to the
children of those affected is only gradually being collected.
There are a number of instances where an affected individual
has had one affected child, and several where they have had
two effected or even three affected children.

Two such families are shown in Figure 71, both coming
to notice at the same children's hospital. The mother in

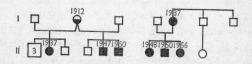

71. Two pedigrees of pyloric stenosis: mother and
children affected

the first pedigree, I, 2 born 1912, was one of the few survivors before the invention of the best operation for the
abnormality. In the other pedigree the mother and all
her affected children were successfully treated by operation. These families are, however, exceptional and it is now
clear that the risk to sons and daughters is of the same order
as that to brothers and sisters, though more information is
needed before this may be regarded as well-established. It is
also apparent, that the proportion of affected is much higher
among the children of the relatively rare girl patients.
About 1 in 5 of their sons and 1 in 10 of their daughters have
the disease, compared with 1 in 20 of the sons and 1 in 50 of
the daughters of boy patients. Turning to other relatives, the
risk to nephews and nieces is probably raised, but the risk to
first cousins may be little more than that to members of the
general population.

Only a small number of twin studies are available for

yloric stenosis, but they are sufficient to show that the
roportion of identical co-twins also affected is well below
00 per cent and probably below 50 per cent. It is almost
ertainly higher, however, than for fraternal twins where the
roportion affected is similar to that of non-twin brothers
nd sisters. There is, therefore, a strong indication that gene-
ic factors play a part in the causation of pyloric stenosis.
he twin studies show that environmental factors must also
e concerned, and that perhaps one half or more of those who
ave the genetic predisposition never develop symptoms of
he condition. While several genetic hypotheses would fit the
acts observed, the best fit is given by multifactorial inheri-
ance with a threshold. In addition this would account neatly
or the much increased risk to the near relatives of girl
atients. These affected girls must be more extreme deviants
rom the population average than the boys.

Little is yet known about the environmental factors con-
erned in causing this illness. One clue is that the illness comes
n earlier in babies born at home than in those born in hos-
ital. Another that the condition tends to develop earlier in
abies fed three-hourly than those fed four-hourly. Yet
nother is that where the condition develops after the first
ortnight, it is more common in first-born children. These
ll suggested that skill in the feeding of the baby in the first
ortnight plays some part in determining whether the genetic
redisposition leads to frank illness.

## Congenital dislocation of the hip

Like pyloric stenosis, it is usual to include this condition
mong congenital malformations, though in many instances
he actual dislocation is not present at birth. The condition is
ather less common in this country than harelip, affecting
bout 1 child in 1,500. In contrast to pyloric stenosis and
arelip, it is much more common among girls than boys. The
atio is about six girls affected to one boy and the propor-

tion of girls affected is about 1·1 per 1,000 and of boys 0·2
per 1,000. As with many other malformations the frequency
varies in different parts of the world. In Europe it is especially common in northern Italy and the highest frequencies
have been reported for Lapps and Red Indians. It is rare
among Negroes.

Another excellent twin study carried out by Idelberger
in southern Germany has shown that a little less than half
the identical co-twins of affected individuals are also affected.
The fraternal co-twins' risk is like that for non-twin brothers
and sisters: 1 to 2 per cent for boys and 5 to 10 per cent for
girls. The risk to the children of affected individuals is of
about the same order and that to parents rather lower. The
risk to cousins is considerably less, but still about five times
that in the general population. There are individual families
in which the risks are much higher. There are indications of
two sets of genetic predisposing factors, one favouring the
development of a shallow hip socket, one leading to an unusual elasticity of the ligaments around the joint. The children with the high risk of developing dislocation appear to be
those who inherit both predispositions.

There has been some success in finding clues to the environmental factors. The defect occurs more often among first-
born than later-born children. It is rather more common
among children born breech first than among those born
head first; nearly all first-born children in the breech position
have lain in the mother's womb with their legs bent at the
hip and extended along the trunk. The condition is more
common among children born in winter than those born in
summer. The greater frequency among first- and breech-
born children at first suggested that the actual mechanics of
birth predisposed to the condition. This is probably not so,
as it occurs also among children born by Caesarean operation and it is the abnormal lie of the foetus in the mother's
womb that is important. The association with season of

birth is interesting and one suggestion here is that this is a post-natal influence and the babies born in winter are liable to be tightly wrapped in bed clothes with their legs straight, instead of lying with their hips bent and turned out. Lapps and some Red Indians swaddle their children very tightly.

*Congenital deafness*

A remarkably complete survey was made of congenital deafness in Northern Ireland by Stevenson and Cheeseman from the Queen's University, Belfast, and reported in 1956. About 1 child in 3,000 is born deaf. In a small proportion this is due to the mother catching German measles early in the pregnancy. In many, probably the majority, the deafness is genetically determined. The hereditary factor responsible is often a recessive gene, but not always the same recessive gene. Evidence for this is that where both parents are normal they are often first cousins. In the Ulster survey this was true of 10 per cent of such parents, as compared with only about 0·4 per cent in the general population. This raised frequency of cousin marriage incriminates recessive genes but also indicates that more than one such gene must be concerned. If it were always the same gene, the number of carriers in the population would be so high that one would not expect this increase of cousin marriage in the parents of deaf children. Again, if the same recessive gene were always responsible, when two congenitally deaf people married, as they not uncommonly do when educated in the same school for the deaf, all their children should be deaf; if both parents are homozygous for the same gene, all the germ cells they form will carry the gene and all the children will be homozygotes. Of thirty-two marriages which were fertile in the Ulster survey, in only five were all the children deaf, in six there were some normal and some deaf, and in twenty-one all the children were normal. The twenty-one with all normal children can easily be explained if the parents were homozygous for different genes. The six mixed families are explained if one parent was also a carrier of the gene causing deafness in the other. This was the explanation favoured in the Ulster survey, but there are points in favour of the alternative hypothesis that the deafness of one or other parent was, in some instances, due to a dominant gene.

If one assumes that recessive genes are responsible for all the genetically determined types of deafness, then, by comparing the proportion of brothers and sisters affected with the expected 1 in 4 risk, it is possible to calculate that all but about a quarter of instances of congenital deafness are genetically determined. If it is assumed that in some instances a dominant gene is concerned, the proportion genetically determined might be somewhat less, though still considerable.

Part of one of the most interesting of the Ulster pedigrees is shown in Figure 72. It will be seen from this pedigree that

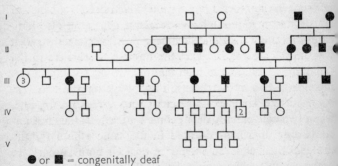

● or ■ = congenitally deaf

72. Part of one of Stevenson and Cheeseman's pedigree of congenital deafness

the deaf husband and wife I, 3 and I, 4 were probably homozygous for the same recessive gene, and this was also the case with II, 10 and II, 11. But the deaf husband and wife in the third generation, III, 9 and III, 10, had unaffected boys and

o were affected by different, though in all probability recessive, genes.

Unfortunately, no way has yet been found of detecting hose who are heterozygous for the recessive genes causing ongenital deafness.

# CHAPTER 14

## Looking to the Future – Eugenics

ANY new advance in scientific knowledge brings a new moral
responsibility to mankind to apply this knowledge correctly.
This is as true of human heredity as it is of nuclear fusion.
The moral issues arising from genetic knowledge are often
difficult, but sooner or later they must be faced. There are
three processes which will bring these issues increasingly to
the fore. The first is that the environmental causes of illness such as malnutrition and bacterial infection are being
prevented. The illnesses which are to a significant degree
genetically determined, even if no more numerous than before, are responsible for an increasing proportion of all
sickness and malformation. The second is that in the near
future, as the genetically determined and in part genetically
determined disorders are successfully treated, they will tend
to become more numerous. Fewer of the mutant genes present in each generation are eliminated, and the proportion of
children born with the adverse genetic predisposition will, in
most instances, increase unless counter measures are taken.
The third is that, with the change from natural to planned
parenthood, artificial selection is, to a large extent, replacing
natural selection. Little is yet known of the direction and intensity of this artificial selection, but it would be risky to
assume that it is negligible.

There need be no hesitancy about one application of human genetics. This is the special investigation and treatment
of those who are known from their family background to be
likely to be predisposed to certain types of illness. An example is the testing of younger brothers and sisters of children who are unable to use milk sugar, so that if the brothers

nd sisters have the abnormality they may be kept on a diet
ree from milk sugar. A much older example is the provision,
n ancient Jewish tradition, that boys from families in which
aemophilia occurs are excused circumcision. The next half
entury will see great strides in protection of this kind from
he common diseases, such as duodenal ulcer, sugar diabetes,
nd perhaps schizophrenia and manic depressive insanity,
vhere development may be due to both genetic predisposition
nd environmental factors. Mankind has an obvious moral
luty to apply genetic knowledge in this way, even though it
educes natural selection against harmful genes.

Human genetics, however, will find its main application in
he attempts to ensure that as many children as possible in
ach generation are born free of genetic predisposition to
bnormal development, and positively endowed with a good
genetic constitution for health and socially valuable qualities
of mind. In doing this, man will gradually be taking control
ver his own evolution, substituting some form of artificial
election for the natural selection which has controlled gene
requencies in the past. This ideal of altering the gene frequencies in the interests of future generations is as morally
ound as the ideal of providing a better environment for
ach successive generation. Many people, however, including
geneticists, have doubts about any deliberate policy of arti-
icial selection. There are three reasons for these doubts.
Many men and women are unable to visualize methods of
artificial selection which are morally right: they doubt
whether artificial selection can be effective in achieving its
aims: and perhaps, most fundamental, they doubt whether
mankind can know just what qualities will be valuable in the
future.

## Aims of artificial selection

Taking the last doubt first, it is true that one generation cannot know in detail the qualities which will be most needed

in the unpredictable future. Probably each new generation
will somewhat alter its aims. There are, however, already
certain aims on which most of us would agree. We would
wish to see fewer children born with genetic predisposition
to severe physical malformation and severe mental deficiency.
On the positive side, most of us would value: the quality of
general intelligence, using intelligence in the sense of the
quality that enables us to find the right solutions to new
problems and difficulties as we meet them; mental stability
in the sense of the quality that enables us to withstand severe
stress, emotional, intellectual, and physical without mental
breakdown; the qualities of courage, energy, and perseverance. On the physical side, resistance to disease, the ability
to live in comfort in varied climates, and good coordination
of nerve and muscle are qualities most of us would like to see
in our children. In communities with a democratic and liberal
tradition artificial selection will proceed from the deliberate
choice of parents planning the size of their families. Once
eugenic responsibilities are generally accepted, progress will
be along the lines of majority opinion and will reflect the
changing ideas of each generation, as well as following differing lines in different countries.

## Methods of artificial selection

It is understandable that people should have doubts on the
methods of artificial selection, since most of the schemes
proposed in the past have been authoritarian, imposed by
governments and involving restrictions on personal liberty.
Several governments have forbidden marriage of men and
women with certain complaints believed hereditary, while,
recently and deplorably, in National Socialist Germany
many men and women were compulsorily sterilized in the
interest of 'Race Hygiene'.

Marriage restriction and sterilization are not necessarily
unethical. Marriages are already forbidden in most countries

etween close relatives, and it might not be unreasonable to
iscourage marriage between couples who are both known
o be carriers of the same recessive gene, where it causes
evere handicap in the homozygote. Voluntary as opposed
o compulsory sterilization is no infringement of liberty, and
, extensively practised in the Scandinavian countries on
enetic indications. In Britain voluntary sterilization on these
rounds is not unknown, but there is still an element of doubt
bout the legality of the operation, except where performed
a the interests of the patient's own health.

Both restriction of marriage and voluntary sterilization,
owever, are likely to become dead issues as methods of
lanning become simpler and more readily available. Artifi-
ial selection will be effected, and is already to some extent
eing effected, through the voluntary choice of family size by
ndividual parents. Where parents have more children than
he average, the genes they carry will in general be more
ommon in the next generation. If they have less than the
verage number of children, the frequency of the genes they
arry will tend to drop in the next generation.

It is sometimes thought that the Churches disapprove of
amily planning. This is not so. The attitude of the Anglican
hurch to family planning has been clearly and positively
tated at the 1958 Lambeth Conference. The resolution reads:

The Conference believes that the responsibility for deciding upon
ne number and frequency of children has been laid by God upon
ne consciences of parents everywhere: that this planning, in such
ays as are mutually acceptable to husband and wife in Christian
onscience, is a right and important factor of family life and should
e the result of positive choice before God.

he head of the Anglican church made it clear that he con-
idered it may be the duty of some parents to plan large fami-
es. It is to be presumed, though it has not been explicitly
ated by the Church, that eugenic considerations are one of

the factors parents should consider in planning the size 
their families. The Roman Catholic church has also e
plicitly stated that parents must bear in mind eugen
considerations in planning the size of their families, but en
phasizes that the means used for family planning must be 
conformity with natural law. Such natural methods a
effective for controlling total family size, though spacing t
children may be more difficult.

## Effectiveness of artificial selection for conditions due to sing gene effects

Turning from the methods of artificial selection to the
effectiveness, this will depend on three factors: the degree 
which variation in the quality desired is inherited, the mod
of inheritance, and the completeness with which the artificia
selection is carried out. With most disorders essentially du
to mutant genes it is reasonably straightforward to wor
out the effect of selection on gene frequencies and on th
proportion of children born with the disorder. Some predic
tion is also already possible with qualities such as intelligenc
as measured by intelligence test, where much of the variatio
in the population is due to genetic variation and inheritance 
multifactorial. With other qualities, such as courage an
perseverance, for which the degree of genetic determinatio
and the mode of inheritance are unknown, little can b
predicted at the moment. It is probable, however, that selec
tion would lead to improvement in average genetic endow
ment for the quality desired, at a rate at which we can onl
guess.

Taking first disorders essentially due to mutant genes o
large effect, the potential response to artificial selection ma
be followed from the principles given in Chapter 5. The rela
tionships between the proportion of children born with th
abnormal genes, the mutation rate, and the intensity o
selection apply whether the selection is natural or artificia

*Dominant mutations*

For conditions due to a dominant mutation, if patients voluntarily limit their families so that they have, on the average, only half as many children as the ordinary man and woman, their biological fitness is reduced by half and the proportion of children born affected with the condition will settle to four times the mutation rate. The artificial selection would be as efficient as a natural selection by which half those affected died from the condition, while the remainder had families of usual size. Thus, the tendency of some new treatment to increase the fitness of children affected by a disease due to a dominant mutation, and to lead to an increase of the frequency of the disorder, may be met by advising parents of the risk to their children.

Such artificial selection is essential if any long-term benefit is to be gained from a new treatment. Without it the proportion of children born affected will steadily rise till sufficient children die of the condition, in spite of the better treatment, to balance the number of fresh mutations entering the population. For example, if the fitness of those with familial polyposis of the colon is, without treatment, about half, then the proportion of children born affected will be $4m$, perhaps something like 1 in 25,000. If fitness is raised to nine-tenths, as a result of operative removal of the colon in childhood, then, without artificial selection, the proportion of children born affected in the next generation would rise to $2m$ (from fresh mutations) plus $\frac{9}{10} \times 4m$ (children born to survivors), that is $5 \cdot 6m$; in the next generation it would be $7 \cdot 04m$. This rise would go on until the proportion of children affected was $20m$, perhaps 1 in 5,000, when once again there would be enough individuals dying from the condition, before their reproduction was complete, to balance the fresh mutations coming in in each generation. The disorder would be responsible for as many deaths as before, the lowered risk for the individual patient being balanced by the greater number of men and women born predisposed to develop the condition.

Artificial selection would entirely alter the picture. If fitness was held to half by this means, the proportion of children born with genetic predisposition would not alter following the new treatment, and nine-tenths of these children would survive.

Neither natural nor artificial selection, however, can reduce the proportion of children born affected with conditions due to dominant mutant genes, below that due to fresh mutations, since no way is yet known of reducing mutation rates appreciably.

## Recessive mutations

With completely recessive mutations essentially the same principles apply. But the effect of any change in the intensity of selection on the proportion of carriers of the gene, and of children affected because they are homozygotes for the gene, is very slow. This applies both to the rise in gene frequencies in the population following on effective new treatments and the fall following artificial selection. This is because most of the mutant genes in a population are present in heterozygous carriers and so not subject to selection.

It is necessary to warn parents, after they have had one affected child, of the one in four risk to further children if the condition is a serious one. In these days of small families, however, this will reduce the proportion of affected children only by about one-sixth, and will have little effect on the gene frequencies. Again, where children are successfully treated for some condition due to the homozygous state of a recessive gene, so that they grow up and are capable of having children, if they marry an unrelated person, the risks to these children are small. It is not reasonable to expect much artificial selection against the gene from their voluntarily limiting the size of their families.

The position is greatly altered once it is possible to detect

the heterozygous carriers. Not only will this make it possible
to warn young carriers of the same recessive mutant gene
from marrying each other, and so decrease the proportion
of children born homozygous for these genes, but it will also
make possible artificial selection against these genes in heterozygotes. If these heterozygotes for a particular recessive
gene plan a family size below the average of the population,
the carrier frequency will fall until the carrier frequency is
some small multiple of the mutation rate. Then the birth of
homozygotes would be very rare indeed, even without any
advice to carriers against marrying each other. For example,
with a typical severe recessively determined condition with
frequency of about 1 in 50,000, and so a carrier frequency in
the population of about 1 in 112, artificial selection reducing
the fitness of heterozygotes to two-thirds would, from the
formula for dominance, reduce the carrier frequency to
about 1 in 8,000 ,and the proportion of affected homozygotes
to about 1 in 250,000,000.

It must be remembered, however, that most of the population are heterozygous for one or more recessive genes. It
would only be practical, therefore, to exercise artificial selection individually against those that are unduly common, such
as the gene for Mediterranean anaemia in Italy, sickle-cell
anaemia in parts of Africa and India, and perhaps fibrocystic
disease of the pancreas in this country. Once this selective
advantage of the heterozygote, which has made the serious
illnesses due to the homozygous state of these genes common,
disappears, natural selection by itself will gradually diminish
their frequency. But this involves deaths, and artificial selection is much to be preferred.

Once recessive genes can be detected in the heterozygote,
however, the practical method will probably be to invoke
artificial selection against them in sum, rather than individually. The means would be to assess the total number of
disadvantageous genes a couple carried between them, and

then to suggest to those who carried many more than the average, that they should aim at two children or less, and to those who carried many fewer than the average, that they should aim at three children or more. In giving advice of this kind care would be needed to preserve those recessive genes which are still advantageous in the heterozygous state.

## Sex-linked recessive mutations

With sex-linked recessive genes, once again artificial selection will be really effective only when it is possible to detect the carriers. Its maximum effectiveness, then, will be that the proportion of boys born with the mutant gene may be reduced to the level of the mutation rate. This would come about if all carrier mothers were detected and none had children.

To sum up, the potential effectiveness of artificial selection for mutant genes of large effect is that, in time, it will be possible to reduce the proportion of children born with dominant genes for disordered growth to nearly twice the mutation rate: the proportion of boys with sex-linked recessive genes for disordered growth to near the mutation rate; and practically to eliminate children born homozygous for recessive mutant genes altogether. This is all a long way ahead, and in the meantime perhaps the aim should be to prevent by artificial selection the tendency for the proportion of children born with disadvantageous mutant genes to rise as a result of better treatment. It is also desirable to limit actual increase in the mutation rate from the artificial increase in radiation to which man is now subjecting himself.

## Chromosome abnormalities

The eugenic aspects of the conditions so far known to be due to abnormalities of the chromosomes are similar to those for conditions due to dominant mutations of large effect. The great majority of patients affected by these abnormalities do not reproduce. The main hope for eugenic action is from the discovery and, where possible, the prevention of factors leading to the formation of the abnormal germ cells. In the future it may be possible to screen most pregnancies at about the fourth week for chromosome abnormalities and terminate those where the child would be severely handicapped.

*Artificial selection for qualities with multifactorial inheritance*

Let us turn from abnormalities of development due to chromosome abnormalities and to mutant genes of large effect, to the normal variation in the population for qualities of mind and character that help a child to become a useful and happy individual. Once again the desirable method of artificial selection will be through parents planning their family size with due attention to the genetic endowment they will transmit. The emphasis here, though, will not be the negative one of planning a small family or even none at all, in order to cut down the frequency in the population of disadvantageous mutant genes, but the positive one of planning an above-average size family because the children are likely to be at the upper end of the normal variation for the desirable qualities.

Genetic endowment for qualities such as mental stability, energy, and intelligence is likely to be multifactorial. But provided a considerable proportion of the variation for these qualities in the population is due to this kind of inheritance, then one may predict the effects of selection with reasonable confidence, at any rate for two or three generations. Due allowance must be made for environmental changes and the direct environmental effect of differences in family size on development of these qualities. One may take general intelligence as an illustration, because it can be roughly measured, though it is only one of the desirable qualities. We have seen there is already evidence that much of the variation for intelligence in a population such as that of Britain today is genetic, and that this genetic variation is probably multifactorial.

If one disregards for a moment environmental variation and assumes that the regression towards the mean of a child's intelligence on one parent's intelligence is about half, it is easy to see that differences in fertility in relation to the intelligence of even just one parent would most probably have a considerable effect. To take an extreme example of selection through males; if all the children of the next generation were born to fathers at the lower end of the normal distribution of intelligence, with intelligence quotient about 60, then the average intelligence of the children would be around 80, and half of them would be below this level instead of only about one child in six. Similarly, if all children were born to fathers with intelligence quotient about 140, the average intelligence of the children would be about 120, and half would be above this level instead of only about one child in six. The same procedure applied to the next generation would change the averages to about 70 and about 130. The social consequences of a change of average intelligence of this size in either direction would be enormous.

Such extreme selection is most unlikely to be applied to any human society except in some dire emergency. In practice, too, since as much as a half of the variation in intelligence in present society is environmental, part only of the change would be due to change in gene frequencies. The experience of animal breeders for such characters is that at first rapid changes can be brought about in the way we have indicated by intense selection, but that after a varying number of generations the effect of selection becomes less than one would expect and is often hampered by loss of fertility. There is no evidence that natural selection has yet had this effect in relation to intelligence in man. The potential fertility of men and women of high intelligence today is certainly sufficient to permit most of them, if they wish, to fulfil plans for a large family, and there is little doubt that artificial selection could have considerable effects on the level of intelligence of the population. Part at least of this effect would represent genetic change.

In the discussion on natural selection in relation to intelligence in Chapter 7, it was suggested that the practice of deliberate family planning is effectively adopted first by the most intelligent and competent parents in the population. For a time, therefore, it results in an association of high intelligence and relative infertility balancing any natural selection whereby the less intelligent and less competent lose more of their children by death in childhood. It was also suggested that a counter trend has already developed within the group practising effective family planning whereby, on the whole, the more intelligent parents are having more children. If, as seems probable, few of the intelligent parents are at present consciously influenced by eugenic ideas, this may illustrate an important feature of artificial selection through family planning. Once all children are planned, even though the parents have no deliberate eugenic policy, it is to be expected that, on the whole, those parents who are likely to transmit socially valuable qualities will have the largest families.

Generally speaking, it is the mothers who are competent, energetic, and mentally stable, as well as being fond of children, who will find the rearing of their first two or three children enjoyable and rewarding and will plan further children. Again, parents who have qualities which are especially valuable to the community will, in general, be well paid. They will be able to afford large families. Even when they are not well paid, like many clergymen and creative artists, they are the kind of people who carry through their plans for the size of their families despite financial or other difficulties. Even so, parents' plans will be influenced by the social policies of the community in which they live and governments will be well advised to consider the effects of their health, educational, and housing policies on the genetic structure of the coming generations of children.

## Eugenically desirable policies

MEDICAL: It is most important to make knowledge of and facilities for family planning, appropriate to the individual's religion, available to the community as soon as possible. Special efforts are needed to offer the opportunity of family planning to the most ignorant and least gifted groups. This will be much more easily done once a simple and reliable method of contraception has been found. Facilities for medical genetic counselling should also be expanded.

SOCIAL: It is important to investigate, as far as possible, social circumstances which may lead good parents, unwillingly, to limit their families to two or three children lest they prejudice the opportunities of these children. Inevitably bringing up a large family of four or more children taxes the energy and resourcefulness of the parents, particularly the mother. This is desirable, since then only mothers well endowed in these respects will wish to go beyond a two- or three-child family. But it is undesirable from the viewpoint of eugenics that good parents, who rightly have a feeling of responsibility for their children's welfare, should feel they must restrict the size of the family in the interests of the first two or three children. A recent survey of the families of children who were showing unusual promise, in local authority schools in south-east England showed that the main parental anxiety today is not the difficulty of providing material care but of providing the best education for their children. The two most useful measures to meet these anxieties would be to hasten the improvement of local authority schools, and to extend the generous system of educational grants already available for university and other post-school education to all education for suitable children beyond compulsory school-leaving age.

EDUCATIONAL: It is important that the biological sciences should be more extensively and better taught in schools in order that community opinion on the application of human genetics should be well-informed. In a successful agrarian or pastoral community knowledge of essential biological principles is widespread, though often unformulated. In an urban or industrial community biology must be directly taught.

## The far future

While the ways in which knowledge of human genetics will be applied in the near future is fairly clear, one can only guess at the applications of human genetics in the distant future. New discoveries will be made at an increasing rate, as many of the best scientific minds turn from the physical sciences to the more complex but more interesting biological sciences. In addition, if any large populations are successful in using artificial selection to raise average intelligence significantly, all kinds of scientific discoveries will come fast.

In human genetics the most important future discovery will perhaps be ways of inducing at will mutations in any desired direction. On the negative side this would make it possible to change the disadvantageous mutations an individual might possess back to the normal form, so that they will not be transmitted. On the positive side it would make it possible to induce new mutations deliberately to meet new environmental stresses as they arise.

# Suggestions for Further Reading

## GENERAL

STERN, C., *Principles of Human Genetics*, W. H. Freeman, London, 1959.

PENROSE, L. S., *Outline of Human Genetics*, Heinemann, London, 1959.

PENROSE, L. S. (Editor), *Recent Advances in Human Genetics*, Churchill, London, 1961.

## BLOOD GROUPS

RACE, R. R., and SANGER, R., *Blood Groups in Man*, Blackwell, Oxford, 1958.

MOURANT, A. E., *The Distribution of Human Blood Groups*, Blackwell, Oxford, 1954.

## PSYCHOLOGICAL

GALTON, F., *Inquiries into Human Faculty and its Development*, Macmillan, London, 1885.

NEWMAN, H. H., FREEMAN, F. N., and HOLZINGER, K. J., *Twins: A Study of Heredity and Environment*, University of Chicago Press, 1937.

VERNON, P. E., *Intelligence and Attainment Tests*, University of London Press, 1960.

FULLER, J. L., and THOMPSON, W. R., *Behaviour Genetics*, Wiley, London, 1960.

## MEDICAL

ROBERTS, J. A. F., *Introduction to Medical Genetics*, Oxford University Press, 1959.

PENROSE, L. S., *Biology of Mental Defect*, Sidgwick and Jackson, London, 1954.

HARRIS, H., *Human Biochemical Genetics*, Cambridge University Press, 1959.

STEINBERG, A. G. (Editor), *Progress in Medical Genetics*, Grune and Stratton, 1961.


## EUGENICS

BLACKER, C. P., *Eugenics; Galton and After*, Duckworth, London, 1952.

OSBORN, F., *Preface to Eugenics*, Harper and Brothers, New York, 1951.

# INDEX

# Index

## MORE ABOUT PENGUINS
## AND PELICANS

*Penguin Book News*, which appears every month, contains details of all the new books issued by Penguins as they are published. From time to time it is supplemented by *Penguins in Print* – a complete list of all our available titles. (There are well over three thousand of these.)

A specimen copy of *Penguin Book News* will be sent to you free on request, and you can become a subscriber for the price of the postage – 4s. for a year's issues (including the complete lists). Just write to Dept EP, Penguin Books Ltd, Harmondsworth, Middlesex, enclosing a cheque or postal order, and your name will be added to the mailing list.

Some other books published by Penguins are described on the following pages.

Note: *Penguin Book News* and *Penguins in Print* are not available in the U.S.A. or Canada

# MASS, LENGTH AND TIME

## *Norman Feather*

Measurements of mass, length, and time are the fundamental measurements in physics. Professor Feather traces the history of the emergence of these concepts, with their associated systems of measurement, from the earliest times. On this basis the whole subject of the mechanical properties of matter in bulk is developed. A unique feature of the book is its complete exclusion of the calculus, in any formal context. The author's express intention is to provide an understanding of principles and he devotes chapters to different kinds of motion, to force, mass, and inertia, to gravitation, energy of various sorts, elasticity, and surface tension. His biographical notes on the physicists he mentions add direct human interest to this explanation of 'what Physics is all about'. For essentially this book offers a friendly introduction to the science of Physics.

'What the author has in view . . . has been done admirably, in a way that will stimulate the general interest and broaden the mind of the youthful reader' – Professor Andrade in the *New Scientist*.

# ORIGINS AND GROWTH OF BIOLOGY

*Edited by Arthur Rook*

*Origins and Growth of Biology* (based on *Moments of Discovery* by Schwartz and Bishop) is a history of the science of life and the struggle against disease. It was Hippocrates, in the fifth century B.C., who first pronounced that disease, far from being an Act of God, had natural causes and could be treated scientifically. Later Aristotle made formidable additions to the knowledge and understanding of nature. Though the torch of science burned very low in the Dark Ages, it began to flare once again with the dissection work of Andreas Vesalius in the sixteenth century and thereafter the study of the human body, of animals, and plants proceeded at a mounting tempo, in the hands of such great men as Harvey, Linnaeus, Darwin, Mendel, Pasteur, and Lister.

Included in this excellent outline are extracts from the most important writings of the great biologists, as well as brief biographies.

*Origins and Growth of Physical Science*, a two-volume companion to this work, is also published in Pelicans.

# INTRODUCING SCIENCE

*Alan Isaacs*

'It is doubtful if the kind of science included in the general education of humanists is even barely adequate.' So the Duke of Edinburgh expressed a feeling that most of us probably share (with varying degrees of guilt). In this direct, lively book Dr Isaacs introduces science to all those who realize that their understanding of modern life is limited by ignorance of science. He first identified the two great principles of the universe – matter and energy. A whole section of the book is then devoted to each of these concepts. The chapter on living matter takes into account the most recent bio-chemical developments; while the section on energy describes nuclear energy as well as the older forms – chemical, heat, mechanical, and radiant. The final part of the book surveys the boundaries of knowledge, dealing in particular with the creation of life and the ultimate nature of matter.

We live in a scientific age. Can we afford *not* to be introduced to science?

# A DICTIONARY OF ELECTRONICS

*S. Handel*

So rapid has been the growth of electronics that you will not find the word in any English dictionary published before 1940. 'Transistor' is still absent from most dictionaries. Yet both words are in common use, though often not understood.

Automation, radar, television, tape-recording, computers, artificial satellites, guided missiles, communications, and navigation – all these, with their profound effect on everyday life, are dependent on electronics, and each application contributes its quota of new words. Hence we have a serious problem of language.

This dictionary has been prepared by a consultant electrical engineer, with twenty years' experience in electronics, as a concise, accurate, and up-to-date reference work both for those who are professionally concerned with electronics and for those who are simply moved by a healthy curiosity about our complicated world. In the definitions provided, such words and phrases as may be unfamiliar to non-technical readers are all related, by systematic cross-reference, to 'standard dictionary' words. Specialists in electronics will find this a useful source of short, authoritative descriptions and, when they exist, standardized descriptions.